D0546031

ABOUT THIS BOOK

SUBJECT MATTER

This book presents an introduction to English Grammar via the forms and usage of the parts of speech.

In the process, it is designed to help in the development of vocabulary and spelling, comprehension skills and sentence construction; and to give an insight into the workings of many foreign languages. A great deal of information has deliberately been included, in a precise but readable manner, and using formal terminology.

The book will provide the children using it with a knowledge of the structure of their own language. Knowledge is power, and understanding *how* the language works will give those children the ability to use English for themselves far more effectively.

LAYOUT

The format is that of a (re-usable) workbook. Each double page provides a factsheet on a particular topic, facing a worksheet designed both to test the knowledge provided and to help the child in its use. Putting the two together makes reference back very simple. Testsheets to monitor progress are provided at the end of the book, together with an index and glossary.

USE

The factsheets may be used directly by the child as an information source. Alternatively they may be used to provide the basis of the teaching content of a lesson, or as reinforcement to the teacher's own lesson plans and scheme of work.

The worksheets are intended to be used by children working alone or in groups, with support and assistance available from the teacher (or parents).

The book can readily be used for work done at home.

A suggested marking scheme is provided for each exercise and worksheet (with a total of 2,000 marks for the entire 27 worksheets, plus another 500 for the testsheets). Teachers may, of course, wish to vary the weightings given to individual exercises, or to employ their own marking schemes.

However, it is envisaged that the marking of the worksheets *with* the children who have done them will in itself provide a useful teaching vehicle.

AGE/ABILITY RANGE

The content has been intensively tested with pupils as young as nine and as old as 15, with a remarkable degree of success.

More or less support will, of course, be required from the teacher, depending on the age and ability of the children using the book.

The book is best suited to top primary and lower secondary school pupils, or pupils in middle and preparatory schools, in the age range 10+ to 14+ and of average or above average ability. It can also be used as a revision primer for older pupils.

A reading age of 11+ is recommended, and the book would not generally be suitable for use with remedial teaching groups.

FACTSHEET ONE

PARTS OF SPEECH — NOUNS

Every word in English that is spoken or written is a PART OF SPEECH.

Parts of Speech are classified into several different sorts:—

Nouns	— Naming words
Verbs	— Doing words
Adjectives	— Describing words: 'added' to nouns
Adverbs	— Describing words: 'added' to verbs
Pronouns	— Words that take the place of nouns
Conjunctions	— Joining words
Prepositions	— Words that go in front of nouns or pronouns, often to indicate 'position'
Interjections	— Words that are shouted out, or exclaimed
Articles	— *The, a, an:* the three articles (sometimes classified as adjectives).

Every single word in the English language is one of these parts of speech. In this book you will learn a great deal about the different parts of speech. They are the building blocks from which the language is constructed. We start with nouns.

A NOUN IS A NAMING WORD

It may name	A PERSON	— boy, woman, David, Mrs Smith, Tommy Atkins, Khaliq Khan, The Queen, King Edward I
It may name	AN ANIMAL	— dog, cat, Rover
It may name	A PLACE	— house, town, river, sea, London, England, The River Thames, The Gobi Desert
It may name	A THING	— book, table, school, story, grass, dinner, coat, Westminster Abbey, The North Star
It may name	A COLLECTION OF ANIMALS, PEOPLE OR THINGS	— herd, flock, class, bunch, group, audience
It may name	A THING THAT YOU EXPERIENCE, OR FEEL, OR UNDERSTAND	— love, pain, speed, space, delay, danger, imagination, illness, journey, science, vision, thought, distance
It may name	A THING THAT YOU DO	— action, statement, decision, destruction, management, advice

AND ANY OTHER SORT OF THING AT ALL!

(a) Make a list of twenty nouns used to name objects that you can see simply by looking around you at the moment.

(10 — ½ each)

10

(b) Copy down the following sentences, and carefully underline the nouns in them.
There are two nouns in each sentence.

Example: Jimmy is up a tree.   Jimmy is up a tree.

(1) Mary is a tall girl
(2) My cat is called Tiger.
(3) England is a country.
(4) Henry was a bad king.
(5) Read your book, John.
(6) There are thirty people in the class.
(7) Always write in sentences, children.
(8) Too many cooks spoil the broth.
(9) Whose book is this on the floor?
(10) I hope it's chips for dinner.

16

(20 — 2 each)

(c) Copy down these sentences, filling in the gap with a noun. Try to use the noun that makes the best sense. Underline the noun you have put in.

Example: I am doing an.................   I am doing an exercise.

(1) My best friend is called.................
(2) The.................are playing football.
(3) Jenny is wearing a blue.................
(4) Paris is the capital of.................
(5) We have an apple tree in our.................
(6) How many.................are there in this class?
(7) What is the.................? It is three o'clock.
(8) Listen! I can hear a strange.................
(9) English is my favourite.................in school.
(10) I have just seen a terrible.................

20

(20 — 2 each)

(d) In this exercise you have to do exactly the same as in the one before. You may need to think more carefully about the noun you fill in.

(1) Have you ever been for a.................in an aeroplane?
(2) He went on a long.................by ocean liner.
(3) The racing car has a maximum.................of 250 m.p.h.
(4) The patient is suffering from a serious.................
(5) The express train is about to depart from.................five.
(6) If you do not behave, you will receive a severe.................
(7) This girl shows considerable.................in football.
(8) The shepherd was leading a.................of sheep.
(9) The council came to a.................to increase the rates by five per cent.
(10) It is with great.................that I announce Mrs Green's retirement.

20

(20 — 2 each)

FACTSHEET TWO

NOUNS (2)

Some nouns are hard to recognize, or to think of. They are usually those mentioned at the end of the list on Factsheet One — things you experience, feel, understand or do.

If you are in doubt, look up the word you have been given, or are unsure about, in a dictionary. It will usually help. Also, simply remember that a noun always stands for a 'thing' (even if some of the things are rather strange!)

Some words can be more than one part of speech, depending on the job they are doing in the sentence. Look at this example:—

The pupils all gave a loud laugh, which echoed round the schoolroom.
"Did you laugh at my singing?" demanded Miss Quaverly. "Do not dare to laugh at your teacher, you hideous children!"

The first time it is used, 'laugh' is a noun, — because it is the *name* of the *thing* the pupils gave (even though the teacher didn't want it). When the teacher spoke she used 'laugh' twice, — both times as a verb — a doing word.

Remember: if the word stands for some sort of thing, then it is a noun.

Some nouns are made up of more than one word. This is not as complicated as it sounds. 'New York' is a single noun; so is 'Queen Elizabeth I' and 'The Mountains of Mourne'. You need all the words to give the thing, person or place their real name. (Think about the case of 'New York'. You could hardly just call the place 'New', and if you just called it 'York', it would be somewhere else altogether! You need both bits to complete the noun).

Now read through this passage. All the nouns in it have been underlined, to help you get used to recognizing them. Then try it yourself, picking out nouns from passages in books.

Once upon a time, there was a great king, who lived in a palace in Samarkand, a fine city, far away in the deserts of central Asia. He ruled over wide lands, and possessed great wealth and power. He enjoyed rich food and was given splendid entertainments. All his people bowed down before his golden throne in awe and adoration; all were dazzled by the splendour of his majesty. But the king was bored. One day a thought came into his mind. He decided to change places with a certain poor man, whose name was Ali ibn Yussuf. Ali was very happy with this arrangement, so King Ahmed carried out his plan. In a very short time he found that he did not like his new life. In fact it was terrible. So he asked his replacement on the throne to give him back his kingdom. Ali, who was now the ruler of all his towns and provinces, and the owner of his priceless treasures, gave him this reply:—

"I will give you back all that you own, — as soon as I get bored with it."

4

(70)

(a) In this exercise, fill in the blanks with nouns that make good sense.

    (1)   Stand up the.................who broke that.................!

    (2)   What.................have you put for.................number three?

    (3)   The.................of her new.................was very fashionable.

    (4)   The.................of the submarine was one hundred.................below sea level.

    (5)   What special.................have been made to receive our distinguished.................?   (10 — 1 each blank)

(b) Copy down the following sentences, and carefully underline the nouns in them. In the first five sentences, the number of nouns you must find has been given; in the next five, you will have to do without the clue.

    (1)   The spaceship is now approaching the speed of light.   (3)

    (2)   We must ask the council to repair the drains.   (2)

    (3)   The River Weser washes the walls of Hamelin on the western side.   (4)

    (4)   You can see the Isle of Wight from that hill.   (2)

    (5)   I could not get a clear view because of the fog.   (2)

    (6)   Can you see whether they have arrived yet, Mrs Brown?

    (7)   Listen to me when I am talking to you!

    (8)   He could not give me a satisfactory answer to my question.

    (9)   Those boys are like a herd of cattle.

    (10) Does he never have a wash?

    You should have found SEVEN nouns in numbers 6 to 10 (and there was one trick question!)   (20 — 1 per noun)

(c) Write out the sentences and underline the nouns once again. There are four in each.

    (1)   Downing Street is in London, the capital of Great Britain.

    (2)   Our soldiers are in serious danger of attack by the enemy.

    (3)   My friend has been for a flight in Concorde to the United States.

    (4)   The destruction of the playground was a disgraceful act of vandalism.

    (5)   We can no longer delay the decision to appoint a new person as supervisor of the canteen.

            (20 — 1 per noun)

(d) Look through this list of words carefully, and write down all those that *could* be nouns. (Some might also be other parts of speech as well; some are only nouns).

| silence | hand | Wednesday | fly | lend | on | us | stream | play |
| weigh | after | naughty | teach | sink | dog | sing | Adam | watch |

            (10)

(e) Write out this little story, and underline all the nouns in it. (There are ten.)

    "John has a pain in his knee, teacher!"

    "Oh dear! How did he do that? Did he fall over in the playground? Did he bang it on the desk, — or has he cut himself on a sharp piece of stone?"

    "No, he was trying to burn his trousers with a magnifying glass . . . . . ."

            (10)

FACTSHEET THREE

NOUNS AND ARTICLES

There are three ARTICLES:— <u>THE</u> <u>A</u> <u>AN</u>

They stand in front of nouns (though sometimes other words come between a noun and its article, as in:— *the clever girl*).

<u>THE</u>   tells you that the noun which follows it is a particular or special one of its kind.

<u>A</u>   tells you that the noun which follows it could be any one of that sort of thing.

<u>AN</u>   is used instead of <u>A</u> when the following word begins with a vowel (a, e, i, o, u).

'THE' is known as the DEFINITE article; 'A' and 'AN' as the INDEFINITE articles.

<u>A</u> and <u>AN</u> cannot be used for plural nouns, — that is when more than one thing is being mentioned.

<u>THE</u> can be used for singular and plural nouns, — one thing or several.

So, you can say: A MAN or AN EXAMPLE, but you *cannot* say A MEN or AN EXAMPLES.

On the other hand, you can say THE BOY and THE BOYS, THE WOMAN and THE WOMEN.

NOUNS DO NOT NEED TO HAVE AN ARTICLE AT ALL. They often manage perfectly well without one.

Nouns which stand for things you cannot see, touch, hear, etc., quite often have no article. Names of people and places very often have no article. When they do have one, it often becomes part of the noun (as in 'The Queen').

Nouns standing for one thing (singular nouns) are more likely to have an article than those standing for more than one (plural nouns).

Use an article if it makes sense to do so. Sometimes the use of an article is a matter of your choice. Sometimes putting in an article, or leaving one out, will make what you are writing look very strange. When you do use an article, pick the one that makes the best sense. Never write things like 'an story' or 'a toys'.

The articles provide a useful way of seeing if a word is a noun or not. Try putting *THE* in front of a word. If it makes sense with *THE*, it is a noun!

Now read through this passage. The articles have been underlined. Where there is a noun without an article, an asterisk (a small star, like this *) has been put in front of it.

One * day <u>a</u> girl was sent to <u>the</u> shops by her * mother. She was rather <u>a</u> silly child. She rarely paid * attention to <u>the</u> things her * mother and * father, or <u>the</u> teachers at * school told her. Now, her * mother had told her to buy * apples, * oranges, <u>a</u> box of * dates, and ten * pounds of * potatoes. <u>The</u> girl did not listen properly to <u>the</u> instructions. She caught <u>a</u> bus to <u>the</u> nearby town, and as she sat singing to herself on <u>the</u> top deck, all * thought of <u>the</u> things she had to buy drifted out of her empty * head. She arrived in * town, got off <u>the</u> bus, went into <u>a</u> supermarket, and bought what she thought was right. She went back with <u>a</u> box of * apples, ten * pounds of * dates, and <u>a</u> single potato, — all in <u>an</u> orange carrier bag!

(a) In each space indicated by an asterisk (*), either insert one of the articles (A, THE, AN), or do not insert anything if you do not think an article is needed. When you write out the correct sentence, underline the articles you have put in.

(1) He is (*) naughty boy.

(2) Can I have (*) orange?

(3) Where are (*) sausages?

(4) Look at (*) seagulls.

(5) Does he have (*) pen?

(6) Do they have (*) pens?

(7) (*) sugar is not good for you.

(8) He did not give (*) very good answer.

(9) That is (*) right choice.

(10) Everyone must choose (*) partner.

(10)

(b) Now, for revision, make a list of all the nouns in the above exercise.   (5 — ½ each)

(c) This is the same as exercise (a). Insert one of the articles, or make no insertion if you do not think an article is needed, where an asterisk (*) is shown. You will find this one quite a bit harder!

(1) (*) enemy are attacking (*) castle of (*) Sir Giles.

(2) He was awakened from (*) deep sleep by (*) eerie howls of (*) pack of (*) wolves in (*) distant hills.

(3) (*) land was wrapped in (*) silence, as (*) waves broke noiselessly over (*) rocks at (*) foot of (*) cliffs.

(4) It is essential that we reach (*) decision on (*) question before us.

(5) (*) new ideas for (*) alternative design flashed through (*) quick mind of (*) Miss Patel.

(20 — 1 per article)

(d) Another, harder piece of revision: once again, write down all the nouns in the exercise you have just done.

(10 — ½ per noun)

(e) In the following sentences *all* the articles included are wrong! They have been underlined, so that you will notice them. Rewrite the sentences with the incorrect articles either changed to the correct ones, or left out altogether if you think that no article is necessary.

(1) Alice is the good girl.

(2) A men who look after a sheep are called the shepherds.

(3) Jenny got an new bike for the Christmas present.

(4) A boys like the hard work, don't they?

(5) Always aim for a neatness and the good sense in your work.

(6) A boy who broke a window is to go to an office at a break.

(7) An essay shows the imagination.

(8) The bird in a hand is worth the two in a bush.

(9) The distant light, like a greyness of a dawn, appeared at an end of a tunnel.

(10) A general made a decision to advance after the two hours against an enemy positions in a city of Paris.

(15 — ½ per change)

FACTSHEET FOUR

COMMON NOUNS

Turn back to Factsheet One, and read through again the descriptions of different things that nouns can stand for. In fact all these different things can be sorted into four groups, which make up the four TYPES OF NOUNS. These are:—

COMMON NOUNS
PROPER NOUNS
ABSTRACT NOUNS
COLLECTIVE NOUNS

We will start off with COMMON NOUNS, since they are the simplest. Common nouns stand for any *general* thing, place or person in the world, — the common or ordinary things that you can experience with your senses.

You may be able to *touch* them, like WOOD SEA EARTH GLASS
(though you may be touching some things without realising it, like GAS and WIND, the words still count as common nouns).

You may be able to *see* them, like STAR LIGHT LINE RIPPLE GHOST SHAPE
(Notice that some of these things you definitely cannot touch, but since you can see them the nouns that stand for them are common nouns).

You may be able to *taste* them, like ORANGES SAUSAGES MEAT SALT POISON

You may be able to *smell* them, like PERFUME FLOWER STINK

You may be able to *hear* them, like SONG SHOUT WHISPER UPROAR CLANG

Most objects for which common nouns stand can be experienced with more than one of the senses. You can see *and* touch a chair. You can certainly taste sausages (one of the examples above), but you can also smell them, touch them, see them, — and even hear them when they are cooking!

The obvious way to check a word is a common noun is simply to go through the senses and decide whether you do experience it with one or more of them. But you also need to make sure the word is standing for a *general* thing. Here are some cases where the nouns are not common nouns:—

Real names: — the names of people, places or things, like MR SMITH, or ANNE JONES, or ENGLAND. These are called *proper nouns*. There is no way you can confuse them with common nouns, as they always have capital letters.

Words for groups are not common nouns, but *collective nouns* (for example — HERD, CROWD).

Words for things you understand with your mind (IDEA, SCIENCE), or experience with your emotions (FEAR, HAPPINESS), and for the names of actions (DECISION, RENEWAL, ASSISTANCE) are not common nouns as you can't experience them with your senses. They are known as *abstract nouns*.

(a) In this exercise you are asked to write down various nouns. Do *not* use any of the words given as examples in the Factsheet. Try to think of new ones of your own. Also, do not repeat nouns you have already used.

(1) Write down seven common nouns standing for things you can touch.

(2) Write down seven common nouns standing for things you can see.

(3) Write down three common nouns standing for things you can taste.

(4) Write down three common nouns standing for things you can smell.

(5) Write down four common nouns standing for things you can hear.

(6) Write down two common nouns standing for things you can hear, but *not* touch.

(7) Write down one common noun standing for a thing you can see, but *not* touch.

(8) Write down one common noun standing for a thing you can touch without realising it (such as *gas*).

(9) Write down one common noun standing for a thing you might experience with all of your senses.

(10) Write down one common noun standing for a thing that you could experience with only one of the senses. (For example, you could only hear a *shout*.)

(30)

(b) Write out these sentences, and underline the common nouns in each of them. You should find twenty altogether.

(1) There is too much salt on my sausages!

(2) He smelt the sweet perfumes of the flowers.

(3) When we came out of the wood, we could see the sea.

(4) Every child should go to school.

(5) Be good while I am out of the room, children!

(6) If you do not close that window, we shall all be blown away.

(7) Study hard, or you will never be as clever as your mother.

(8) The smell of the roast in the pot attracted Terry from the garden.

(9) The shouts of the crowd drowned my whisper.

(10) The regular action of the pump soon began to move the water.

(20 — 1 per noun)

(c) This exercise is the same as the one before, but slightly harder.

(1) A strong breeze was blowing the clouds away.

(2) The sound of a motor could be heard in the distance.

(3) All boys are prone to misbehaviour; they need constant discipline.

(4) Miss Williams is a better typist than young Philips.

(5) She spoke with great force about her intentions regarding the operation of the scheme.

(6) Always look in both directions before you cross the road.

(7) Mine eyes have seen the glory of the coming of the Lord.

(8) You will never get a good education unless you work hard at your English.

(9) Never put your trust in the promises of men.

(10) "Choose your weapons, Herr Baron. We fight to the death!"

(20 — 2 per noun)

FACTSHEET FIVE

PROPER NOUNS

All nouns are the names of things. Proper nouns stand for special or particular things, places, and people. In fact, they are the *real names* of those things, places and people.

Proper nouns are always given capital letters. This makes them easy to recognise in a passage you are reading. On the other hand, when you are writing you do have to remember to give them their capitals.

So, *boy* and *city* are common nouns (standing for any boy and any city).

On the other hand, *Jimmy Wilson* (a particular boy) and *Cardiff* (a particular city) are proper nouns.

A *queen* is a common noun, but the *Queen* (meaning one special or particular queen) is a proper noun.

A *pyramid* is a common noun (as it stands for one of any number of pyramids), but the *Pyramids* (meaning those special pyramids in Egypt) is a proper noun.

Here are some more examples. The main thing to remember with all of them is simply — *Proper nouns are all names.*

The names of people (and animals!)	Peter, Susan Smith, Mrs Johnson, Mr Green, Miss Jones, Ranjit Singh Sandhu, Dr MacPherson, Man Friday, Rover, King Kong.
People's special titles	The Prime Minister, Queen Elizabeth II, King John, My Lord, Your Majesty, Kublai Khan, Sir James Jackson, St. John, Lord of the Isles, the Holy Father.
All sorts of place names	Ivy Cottage, Number Ten, the Empire State Building, Station Road, Derby, Three Bridges, Inverness, Moscow, Hampshire, Strathclyde, the Midlands, Wales, Asia, Stow-on-the-Wold, the United States of America, the North Sea, Mount Everest, the New Forest, the Pennines.
Names of companies, shops, businesses, councils, organizations and institutions	Ounsdale School, University College, Marks and Spencer, John Adams and Sons Ltd., Durham County Council, British Rail, Arsenal Football Club, the Royal Navy, the Rose and Crown, the Trades Union Congress.

Then there are:— book titles (A Tale of Two Cities), programmes (News at Ten), plays (A Midsummer Night's Dream), ships (Titanic), planes (Concorde), trains (Flying Scotsman), the days of the week and the months of the year (but not the seasons!)

Notice that little words (the, a, an, of, in, on, and) in the *middle* of longer proper nouns are NOT given capital letters. When the article (*The, A,* or *An*) at the beginning is *part* of the name or title, it also must have a capital letter.

(a) In the following sentences, the proper nouns have not been given their capital letters. Rewrite each sentence, inserting the correct capital letters. Remember, *names* are proper nouns, and must have capital letters.

   (1) "That boy, david thompson, is a constant nuisance in my lessons," said mrs smith.
   (2) After tessa left school, she went on to girton college, cambridge.
   (3) The most successful ruler of the mongols was genghiz khan.
   (4) After an hour's shopping in woolworths, we retired to a dubious café known as "fred's" for some light refreshment.
   (5) Though new york is a great city, it is not the capital of the united states.
   (6) People who believe that this country should not be ruled by a king or queen are called republicans.
   (7) I shall have to write and complain to british telecom about this bill again.
   (8) "Gentlemen, be upstanding for his royal highness, the prince philip, duke of edinburgh."
   (9) He lives at willowtree house, oakwood lane, ashdown, elmshire.
   (10) The wedding of sir tony broke to lady lespender was attended by many distinguished guests, including the earl and countess of bonniebanks.

   (20 — ½ per capital letter)

(b) In each of the following sentences one noun occurs twice, once as a common noun, once as proper noun. Rewrite the sentences, underlining the noun where it is common, and giving it its capital letter where it is proper.

   (1) The shape of a pyramid is well known to anyone who has seen the pyramids of Egypt.
   (2) Among the dukes of England, the duke of Norfolk has pride of place.
   (3) My favourite city is still the city of London.
   (4) The most important religious book of Ancient Egypt was called 'the book of the Dead'.
   (5) The navy of no other country can compare in fighting spirit with the Royal navy.

   (20 — 2 each word)

(c) In this passage there are no proper nouns. Rewrite it, replacing the words in brackets with proper nouns, so that the story both makes sense, and is a bit more interesting!

   It was early in the morning of (a day) when (a woman) crossed (the street), popped into (a shop) for a new pen, and then hurried on into the offices of (her company). She dictated a few letters to (her secretary), telephoned (another company) and (the local council), and then considered her journey by (train) that afternoon to (another town).

   (20 — 2 each)

(d) In this passage, try to do the exact opposite. Replace all the proper nouns — you can recognise them by their capital letter — with common nouns.

   I had been invited to Blackabbey Castle by Lord Debenture, whose home it was. I hastened through Trafalgar Square to Charing Cross station and travelled by the Southern Railway to Ghoulthorpe. I was met by a Mr Feere, who announced that he was the butler. He told me that I must book a room at the 'Cow and Musket', for the ghost of Sir Mortmain had been seen again, and the Marsetshire Constabulary were taking no chances.

   (20 — 2 each)

FACTSHEET SIX

ABSTRACT NOUNS

An abstract noun stands for a thing which is not material, solid, or concrete.

These things exist, but you cannot feel them with your senses. You cannot see, touch, taste, smell or hear them.

They may be things that you experience with your feelings or emotions	pain pity grief sorrow joy love happiness sadness illness fear anger anxiety sympathy desire weariness pleasure dismay laziness
They may be things that you know or understand with your mind	science mathematics algebra history art religion
They may be states you are in	motion danger flight life peace poverty childhood innocence experience
They may be the qualities that a thing or a person has	height hardness speed distance colour justice ability beauty possibility size quality force success cleverness stupidity
They may be the names of actions — the names for things people do	election decision growth reduction addition thought arrangement work measurement organization discussion laughter revenge choice allowance sight vision action

Many abstract nouns could obviously fall into more than one of these categories. Some abstract nouns come very close to being common nouns. (For example, *music* is usually classified as an abstract noun — because it can mean the study or art or science of music; but when it means a collection of pleasant sounds, it sounds very much like a common noun!)

In fact it is not all that difficult to decide whether most nouns are abstract or not. If they have a capital letter, then you will know they are proper nouns; if they are names of groups of things, they are collective nouns; if they are the names of things you can see, touch, taste, smell or hear, — then they are common nouns. The rest are the abstract nouns. You will also notice that many abstract nouns have the same *endings*. You will notice -NESS, -TION, -SION, -ATION, -MENT in the examples above. Try to start recognizing the abstract nouns in passages you read, — and getting to know what they mean. You will find they are often the longer and harder words, partly because they mean complicated things, partly because they often came into English from foreign languages, — especially Latin!

(a) Write down these sentences, and underline the abstract noun in each.

    (1)   The light breeze brought no movement to the ship's sails.

    (2)   What arrangements have been made to meet Mr Davis?

    (3)   This is a difficult choice for you to make, My Lady.

    (4)   I demand compensation for my damaged umbrella.

    (5)   We were in great difficulties as the rebels began to storm the palace.

    (6)   Who is responsible for the destruction of this book?

    (7)   There can be no excuse for what you have done, young man.

    (8)   You have to make allowances for small children.

    (9)   The extraction of a tooth is far from pleasant.

    (10)   I strongly recommend the use of spices when you are cooking the meat.

(20 — 2 each)

(b) There are twenty abstract nouns in the following list. Divide them up into five categories (four words in each):—

    (1)   Things you experience with your feelings and emotions

    (2)   Things that you know or understand   (4)   States you are in

    (3)   Qualities of things   (5)   Names for actions

fear	size	allowance	innocence	geometry	kindness	selection
death	art	pleasure	colour	strength	music	war
sadness	physics	renewal	creation	wealth	boyhood	

(10 — ½ each)

(c) Many abstract nouns end in -NESS, but the ones that have been underlined in the following passage are completely wrong. Rewrite the passage, replacing them with the correct abstract nouns.

    The naughty boy showed great <u>sorriness</u> for his <u>misbehavingness</u>, but he knew he would not escape the <u>angriness</u> of his father. In the <u>peacefulness</u> of his bedroom he waited with great <u>anxiousness</u> for his father's <u>arrivingness</u> home. When he heard the <u>noisiness</u> of the car he shivered in <u>terrifiedness</u>. He could foresee the <u>possibleness</u> that he would be punished with great <u>severeness</u> after what he had done! Then his father walked in and said: "I've had some bad luck today. I've sprained my wrist, and can't use my hand . . ."

(20 — 2 each)

(d) Still on the subject of the *endings* of abstract nouns, see if you can produce three lists of abstract nouns, the first list of those ending in -ITY or -TY, the second those ending in -MENT, the third those ending in -ANCE or -ENCE. Try to get five words in each.

(15 — 1 per word)

(e) The commonest ending for abstract nouns (particularly those standing for actions) is -ION. It has three common variations: -TION (as in election); -SION (as in decision); -ATION (as in organization). Make three lists of abstract nouns with these endings: list (1) for -TION; list (2) for -SION; list (3) for -ATION. Try to get TEN nouns in each list (and no overlapping between lists (1) and (3)!)

(15 — ½ per word)

FACTSHEET SEVEN

COLLECTIVE NOUNS

A collective noun names a group or collection of people, animals, things, or even places. It is normally quite easy to recognise a collective noun, but you may sometimes find it harder to discover the correct collective noun for a particular group. Some groups of people, things and animals have their own special collective nouns (though some of these are not very well-known, and in ordinary writing you will not go far wrong if you use another ordinary noun — like *group,* or *collection* — so long as it makes sense.)

Here are some collective nouns for groups of PEOPLE:-

a *band* of musicians	a *company* of actors	a *bench* of magistrates
a *board* of directors	a *crew* of sailors	a *staff* of teachers
a *choir* of singers	a *gang* of thieves	a *team* of footballers,
a *class* of pupils	or robbers	cricketers or other players

People gathered together for a particular reason also have collective nouns:-

The *audience* at a cinema or theatre; the *congregation* in a church; the *spectators* at a sporting event; any large group of people may be a *crowd,* and a crowd may turn into a *mob!*

You will also find that some collections of people may have several possible collective nouns. A group of soldiers, depending on its size, may be an *army,* a *division,* a *regiment,* a *platoon,* or quite a few others!

Now here are some collective nouns for groups of ANIMALS:-

a *brood* of hens or chickens	a *litter* of cubs or pups	a *pride* of lions or peacocks
a *flock* of birds	a *pack* of wolves or dogs	a *school* of whales
a *flock* of sheep	a *plague* of locusts	a *shoal* of fish
a *gaggle* of geese		a *swarm* of insects, bees or wasps
a *herd* of cattle, deer or horses		a *team* of horses or oxen

The particular name for a group of animals sometimes depends on what that group is doing. A *team* of horses suggests that they are being used for ploughing; you could also speak of a *stud* or *stable* of horses. A *swarm* of bees sounds as if the bees are flying; on another occasion you might want to speak of a *hive* of bees.

Here are some collective nouns for groups of THINGS:-

a *bunch* of flowers or grapes	a *library* of books	a *suit* of clothes
a *fleet* of ships	a *pack* of cards	a *suite* of furniture (or rooms)

There are many others:- you can have a *clump* or a *forest* of trees; a *cluster,* or *galaxy,* or *constellation* of stars; a *sheaf* of corn, but a *stack* of hay; a *string* of beads, or a *rope* of pearls, or a *necklace* of diamonds; a *flight* of stairs and a *chest* of drawers!

To add interest and humour when you write, you can also make up your own collective nouns (on the same principle as 'pride of lions'). You might decide to write about a *mischief* of boys, and a *giggle* of girls; a *worry* of mothers and a *grumble* of fathers. Be careful of using your inventions if you are writing something serious, though!

(a)   Write down the correct collective nouns for groups of the following people, animals and things:-

(1)	directors	(11)	musicians
(2)	pups	(12)	savages
(3)	oxen	(13)	stairs
(4)	drawers	(14)	actors
(5)	deer	(15)	basketball players
(6)	thieves	(16)	people in church
(7)	wasps	(17)	people watching a play
(8)	pearls	(18)	rooms
(9)	peacocks	(19)	herring
(10)	teachers	(20)	hay

(20)

(b)   Write down the things, people or animals that these collective nouns can be used for:-

(1)	plague	(6)	stud
(2)	gaggle	(7)	platoon
(3)	suit	(8)	hive
(4)	crew	(9)	library
(5)	galaxy	(10)	choir

(10)

(c)   Things get a bit harder now. Try to find out (and this will mean asking people) the correct collective nouns for the following groups of people, things, animals (and places). You will not find them on the factsheet!

(1)	angels	(6)	bishops
(2)	cotton	(7)	bread
(3)	eggs	(8)	arrows
(4)	bells	(9)	clans
(5)	acrobats	(10)	islands

(10)

(d)   In each of the following sentences there is one *abstract* noun and one *collective* noun. Copy out the sentences, and after each collective noun write in brackets the word 'collective', and after each abstract noun, the word 'abstract'. It might be a good idea to read through Factsheet Six again before you start!

(1)   It was difficult to judge the mood of the awaiting crowd.
(2)   The crew scaled the ropes with remarkable agility.
(3)   From his position on the mast he could see the sails of the approaching fleet.
(4)   It is important that we proceed quickly to the election of the committee
(5)   The board of directors has decided to accept the offer of Bloggs Ltd.
(6)   A cluster of stars was shining with great brilliance directly overhead.
(7)   The audience responded with applause.
(8)   The arrival of the opposing team was greeted with loud shouts and jeers.
(9)   His suit of clothes was of great age.
(10) The speed with which he shuffled the pack of cards suggested that he was a gambling man.

(40 — 2 per word correctly identified)

FACTSHEET EIGHT

NOUNS — THE PLURAL

Nouns can be SINGULAR — which means they stand for *one* person, place or thing; or they can be PLURAL — which means they stand for more than one person, place or thing.

MOST NOUNS FORM THEIR PLURAL BY ADDING THE LETTER *S*.

BOY — singular: BOYS — plural. Dog — dogs; house — houses; tie — ties; comb — combs.

BUT THERE ARE EXCEPTIONS. Here is a list of the exceptions:—

(1)　NOUNS ENDING IN -*Y* CHANGE THE *Y* TO *I* AND ADD *ES*.
　　　Lady — ladies; party — parties; fly — flies; possibility — possibilities.

But there is an exception to this exception!

(2)　NOUNS ENDING IN -*AY*, -*EY*, -*OY*, -*UY* SIMPLY ADD *S*.
　　　Day — days; chimney — chimneys; toy — toys; guy — guys.

(3)　NOUNS ENDING IN -*X*, -*S*, -*SS*, -*SH*, -*CH* ADD *ES*.
　　　Box — boxes; gas — gases; mass — masses; dish — dishes; church — churches.
　　　(Notice that CH, SH, S, SS, and X are all 'hissing' sounds.)

(4)　*SOME* NOUNS ENDING IN -*F* CHANGE THE *F* TO *V* AND ADD *ES*.
　　　Loaf — loaves; wolf — wolves; shelf — shelves; thief — thieves; leaf — leaves.
　　　SOME NOUNS ENDING IN -*FE* ALSO CHANGE THE *F* TO *V* AND ADD *S*.
　　　Life — lives; knife — knives; wife — wives.

But there are some exceptions!

(5)　*SOME* NOUNS ENDING IN -*F* (OR -*FE*) SIMPLY ADD *S*.
　　　Gulf — gulfs; roof — roofs; chief — chiefs; fife — fifes.
　　　SOME NOUNS ENDING IN -*F* MAKE THEIR PLURAL IN EITHER -*FS* or -*VES*.
　　　Dwarf — dwarfs or dwarves; hoof — hoofs or hooves; scarf — scarfs or scarves.
　　　There is no rule to cover words ending in F; you must get to know each word!

(6)　MOST NOUNS ENDING IN -*O* ADD *ES*.
　　　Hero — heroes; potato — potatoes; echo — echoes; cargo — cargoes.

(7)　BUT NOUNS ENDING IN -*EO*, -*IO* OR -*OO* SIMPLY ADD *S*.
　　　Radio — radios; cameo — cameos; folio — folios; cuckoo — cuckoos.
　　　AND SOME OTHER NOUNS ENDING -*O* ALSO SIMPLY ADD *S*.
　　　Piano — pianos; banjo — banjos; halo — halos; solo — solos.
　　　There is no rule to cover these words; you must get to know each one!

(8)　SOME NOUNS CHANGE THEIR FORM.
　　　Man — men; woman — women; child — children; mouse — mice; tooth — teeth.

(9)　SOME NOUNS HAVE THE SAME SINGULAR AND PLURAL.
　　　Sheep — sheep; deer — deer; salmon — salmon; cannon — cannon.

(10)　NOUNS MADE UP OF SEVERAL WORDS MAKE THE PLURAL FROM THE *MAIN* WORD.
　　　Brother-in-law — brothers-in-law; man-of-war — men-of-war; passer-by — passers-by.

(11)　SOME FOREIGN WORDS HAVE SPECIAL PLURALS (-*US* may become *I*; *UM* and *ON* may become *A*).

(12)　SOME WORDS HAVE TWO PLURAL FORMS (which often have different meanings).
　　　Penny — pence, pennies; shot — shot, shots; genius — geniuses, genii.

(13)　SOME WORDS HAVE NO SINGULAR.
　　　Trousers, Scissors; Spectacles, Victuals.

(a) Check Rule (1) on the Factsheet. Then write down the plurals of the following nouns:—

(1) fly	(3) remedy	(5) supply	(7) duty	(9) propriety
(2) city	(4) ally	(6) army	(8) cry	(10) democracy

(5 — ½ each)

(b) Check Rule (2) on the Factsheet. Then write down the plurals of these nouns:—

(1) boy	(3) valley	(5) survey	(7) ray	(9) donkey
(2) play	(4) key	(6) alloy	(8) dray	(10) buy (as in 'a good buy')

(5)

(c) Check Rule (3) on the Factsheet. Then write down the plurals of these nouns:—

(1) fox	(3) glass	(5) watch	(7) wash	(9) loss
(2) brush	(4) flash	(6) witch	(8) latch	(10) canvas

(5)

(d) Check Rules (4) and (5) on the Factsheet. Then write down the plural of these nouns:—

(1) reef	(3) calf	(5) stuff	(7) sheaf	(9) giraffe
(2) proof	(4) life	(6) belief	(8) fief	(10) elf

(5)

(e) Check Rules (6) and (7) on the Factsheet. Then write down the plural of these nouns:—

(1) grotto	(3) oratorio	(5) trio	(7) volcano	(9) impressario
(2) foe	(4) tornado	(6) tomato	(8) banjo	(10) zero

(5)

(f) Check Rules (8) and (9) on the Factsheet. Then write down the plural of these nouns:—

(1) louse	(3) goose	(5) ox	(7) dozen	(9) cod
(2) mouse	(4) house	(6) trout	(8) swine	(10) grouse

(5)

(g) Check Rule (10) on the Factsheet. Then write down the plural of these nouns:—

(1) rear-admiral	(3) lord chief justice	(5) hanger-on	(7) commander-in-chief	(9) bookcase
(2) chest of drawers	(4) mouse-trap	(6) spoonful	(8) lady-in-waiting	(10) stepson

(5)

(h) Check Rule (12) on the Factsheet. Then write down two possible plurals for each of these nouns:—

(1) cloth	(2) genius	(3) brother	(4) medium	(5) automaton

(10 — 1 each)

(i) Write down the SINGULAR of each of these nouns:—

(1) thieves	(3) children	(5) by-ways	(7) gases	(9) wives
(2) women	(4) glasses	(6) clothes	(8) entities	(10) thanks

(5 — ½ each)

(j) Write out the following passage, changing all the nouns from singular to plural. You will find you need to change some other words as well.

The wedding was attended by a lady of the county and her husband, a man of considerable ability in the field of science. A boy sang an awful solo, beneath a loaf, a fish, a pumpkin and a banana left over from a recent festival on the shelf behind his head. Some polished their spectacles, a mouse appeared from nowhere, and a maid-of-honour fainted.

(20 — 1 per noun)

FACTSHEET NINE

NOUNS — THE POSSESSIVE

If we want to say THE BOOK OF THE BOY in a shortened form we can say THE BOY'S BOOK.

Possession is shown by adding 'S (APOSTROPHE S) to a noun in the SINGULAR. (This is sometimes called the 'GENITIVE' or 'genitive case' of the noun). Many foreign languages put different endings on their words to show the work the word is doing in the sentence. In English the only endings we put on nouns are to show the PLURAL and to show POSSESSION.

But what happens when we have already added a letter *S* to make a noun plural, and we also want to make it possessive?

If we want to say THE BOOKS OF THE BOYS in a shortened form we can say THE BOYS' BOOKS.

With a plural noun ending in S already, we put an apostrophe after the S to show possession.

We do not add another S as well. (So we do not say *The boys's books:* that is wrong.)

Put the apostrophe on the owner, not on the thing owned! (So do not write *The boys books':* that is not just wrong; it is nonsense!)

Notice the difference between these:

(1)   THE BOY'S BOOK (one book belonging to one boy).
(2)   THE BOY'S BOOKS (several books belonging to one boy).
(3)   THE BOYS' BOOK (one book belonging to several boys).
(4)   THE BOYS' BOOKS (several books belong to several boys).

Never use an apostrophe to make a plural.
(Apples', Oranges' and Bananas' for sale! is another nonsense.)

If you want to make the possessive form of a noun that does not have a plural ending in S, just add 'S (*apostrophe S*) as if it were a noun in the singular. E.g. Men's = of the men; children's = of the children; feet's = of the feet.

If a word in the SINGULAR happens to end in S, make its possessive form by adding 'S in the normal way.

Do not be worried about having S followed by 'S in the singular. E.g. Gas's = of a gas; mass's = of a mass.

In the plural: gases' = of several gases; masses' = of several masses.

With proper nouns ending in S, you may either add 'S or simply add an apostrophe. *Mr Sanders' book* and *James's book* are both correct.

As you know, for some nouns you need to make changes in the spelling when you are forming the plural. NEVER make these changes for the possessive form of the SINGULAR.

Singular:		Plural:	
	Lady's = of a lady		Ladies' = of some ladies
	Church's = of a church		Churches' = of some churches
	Box's = of a box		Boxes' = of some boxes
	Hero's = of a hero		Heroes' = of some heroes
	Loaf's = of a loaf		Loaves' = of some loaves

(a) Rewrite these phrases using the possessive form of the noun
(e.g. *The books of the boys = the boys' books*):—

(1)	the song of the girl	(6)	the kennels of the dogs
(2)	the noise of the car	(7)	the equipment of the soldiers
(3)	the leaves of the tree	(8)	the pencils of the pupils
(4)	the light of the moon	(9)	decisions of parliament
(5)	the price of cabbages	(10)	the sentence of the court

(10)

(b) This exercise is the same. Rewrite using the possessive forms:—

(1)	the dress of the lady	(6)	the contents of the shelves
(2)	the spires of the churches	(7)	the expansion of the gasses
(3)	the lair of a fox	(8)	the work of the class
(4)	the notes of the piano	(9)	the beak of the goose
(5)	the teddies of the babies	(10)	the laughter of the children

(10)

(c) In each of these sentences there is a mistake in the use of the apostrophe. There may be an apostrophe missed out, or an apostrophe inserted where it does not belong; or the incorrect use of the apostrophe may have caused an error in spelling. Now correct the sentences!

(1) There are fourteen boy's in our class.
(2) Is this Helens book?
(3) Four boy's books have not been handed in.
(4) Have you collected the boys' books', Stuart?
(5) Take off the boxes lid and see what's in it?
(6) How much are your cabbages'?
(7) Why are you wearing your fathers' wellingtons, Alison?
(8) Do you really take a mans' size in shoes?
(9) My mother is amazed at the price of childrens' clothes.
(10) Anne and Tara will sing the two solos'.

(20 — 2 each)

(d) Change *all* the nouns in these phrases into the plural.
(e.g. *The boy's book* . . . becomes . . . *The boys' books*):—

(1)	The lady's hat	(6)	The knife's edge
(2)	The house's chimney	(7)	The factory's roof
(3)	The mouse's tail	(8)	The hero's victory
(4)	The child's toy	(9)	The man's lunch
(5)	The loaf's crust	(10)	The boss's wife

(10)

(e) This time do the opposite; change *all* the nouns (which are plural) into the singular:—

(1)	The chiefs' wigwams	(6)	The geese's feet
(2)	The horses' hooves	(7)	The men-of-war's cannon
(3)	The angels' haloes	(8)	The boys' shorts
(4)	The policemen's searches	(9)	The women's children
(5)	The wolves' teeth	(10)	The navies' activities

(10)

FACTSHEET TEN

GENDER

Nouns in English all have a gender. They may be:—

MASCULINE	(e.g. *man, king, father*),	i.e. They are MALE
FEMININE	(e.g. *woman, queen, mother*),	i.e. They are FEMALE
COMMON	(e.g. *person, cousin, animal*),	i.e. They could be MALE OR FEMALE
NEUTER	(e.g. *house, shoe, silence*),	i.e. They are THINGS, NOT ALIVE AT ALL.

NOTE:— Do not confuse a COMMON NOUN with the COMMON GENDER. *Shoe* is a COMMON NOUN, but it is certainly NOT COMMON GENDER (as it obviously is not alive); but *animal* is both a COMMON NOUN, and COMMON GENDER (as it is alive, and could be either male or female).

Many words have separate forms for the MASCULINE and the FEMININE:—

Boy (masculine)	:	*Girl* feminine)
Bull (masculine)	:	*Cow* (feminine)
Headmaster (masculine)	:	*Headmistress* (feminine)

In some cases there are two completely separate words for the masculine and the feminine. But it is more common for the feminine to be formed from the masculine. Very many of these feminine forms end in -ESS (some also end in -INE, and a few in -IX).

Notice that there are quite a few words ending in -ER or -OR (meaning someone who does a particular job) which have a feminine form in -RESS (i.e. the letter E or letter O is squashed out by the feminine ending). (E.g. *actor* becomes *actress*).

But also notice that not all words of this sort have separate masculine and feminine forms; *worker* is COMMON GENDER — a worker can be male or female!

Sometimes there may be a general word which is common gender, and separate masculine and feminine forms for the male and female!

Sheep is COMMON (it could be male or female)
Ram is MASCULINE (it means a male sheep)
Ewe is FEMININE (it means a female sheep)

Some PROPER NOUNS which are the *names of people* have MASCULINE and FEMININE FORMS:—
Charles : Charlotte   George : Georgina   Joseph : Josephine.

Personification

We sometimes treat lifeless things as if they were alive. We make them into persons, or 'personify' them.

We often personify ships, planes, cars and trains as Feminine. (We call them 'she').

We also personify abstract nouns, by giving them a capital letter, and turning them into a sort of proper noun.

When we personify abstract nouns that suggest *strength*, we treat them as Masculine — e.g. Age; Winter; The Sun.

When we personify abstract nouns that suggest *beauty*, we treat them as Feminine — e.g. Love; Spring; The Moon.

Families

While we are thinking about gender, we should also notice that there are often special words for the YOUNG of animals (as well as the masculine and feminine). The young of the goat is called a *kid;* the young of an eagle is called an *eaglet*.

Homes

There are also special names for the HOMES of different people or animals! A pig lives in a *sty*, and a horse in a *stable;* a monk lives in a *monastery*, a king in a *palace*.

(a) Write down these words under the headings MASCULINE, FEMININE, COMMON and NEUTER:—

king animal mother house sky lady Steven child master mare Mary
cattle banana decision son-in-law sister passenger teacher thought boar

(20 — 1 each)

(b) Give the feminine forms of these masculine nouns:—

author heir lion peer prince
tiger hunter actor waiter traitor

(5 — ½ each)

(c) Give the feminine forms of these masculine nouns:—

abbot duke emperor master sorcerer
earl postmaster proprietor executor marquis

(5)

(d) Give the feminine equivalents of these masculine nouns:—

bachelor hero husband nephew uncle
Boy Scout stepson wizard tutor lad

(5)

(e) Give the masculine equivalent of these feminine nouns:

sister bride countess ogress nun
squaw landlady maidservant masseuse Czarina

(5)

(f) (i) Give the masculine equivalents of these feminine nouns:—
cow goose heifer hind nanny-goat

(ii) Give the feminine equivalents of these masculine nouns:—
colt stag drake stallion cock-sparrow

(5)

(g) (i) Give the feminine forms of these proper names:—
Cecil Paul Henry Oliver John

(ii) Give the masculine forms of these proper names:—
Christina Frances Victoria Alexandra Clara

(5)

(h) Write down the special name given to the YOUNG of each of the following animals:—
cow dog goose swan cat
deer horse hen owl hare

(5)

(i) Write down the person or animal you would expect to live in these homes:—
palace kennel nest cell hive
convent eyrie caravan set vespiary

(5)

(j) What are the houses or homes of the following called; there are *two* for each:—
clergyman rabbit lion fox Red Indian

(10 — 1 each)

(k) Write down five things (common or abstract nouns) that might be PERSONIFIED. (Don't forget to give each of them a capital letter). Next to each word say whether it should be MASCULINE or FEMININE.

(10 — 2 each)

FACTSHEET ELEVEN

PRONOUNS

Pronouns stand in the place of nouns.

(1) The most common pronouns are the PERSONAL pronouns:—
I, we, you, he, she, it, they; me, us, him, her, them.

(2) Then there are POSSESSIVE pronouns (formed from the personal pronouns):—
mine, ours, yours, his, hers, its, theirs.

(3) Then there are the RELATIVE pronouns:—
who, which, whose, whom, that. (Notice that 'that' can also be a demonstrative pronoun.)

(4) Then there are what might be called DEMONSTRATIVE pronouns:—
this, that, these, those. (These words are pronouns only when they stand by themselves; not when they are attached to a noun. Remember a pronoun replaces a noun.)

(5) Then there are the INTERROGATIVE pronouns (i.e. ones that ask a question):—
who? which? what? whose? whom? (As you will see, these are like relative pronouns, but they ask a question.)

(6) Then there are words which are known as EMPHATIC or REFLEXIVE pronouns. (These are longer forms of the personal pronouns.)
myself, ourselves, yourself, yourselves, himself, herself, itself, themselves.

A pronoun mentions a person, place or thing, without naming it (i.e. without using a noun). With the personal pronouns, try to get used to which SOUNDS right. You will learn the rules for their use later on:
E.g. *He* and *I* are going. — Correct. *Him* and *me* are going. — Incorrect.
The inspector interviewed *them* and *us*. — Correct.
The inspector interviewed *they* and *we*. — Incorrect.

The thing to remember about possessive pronouns is that they stand by themselves to show ownership: It is *mine* — Pronoun; *My* book — Not a pronoun.

Relative pronouns follow a noun to tell you more about it:—
E.g. The man *whom* I am going to see . . .   The mistake *which* I made . . .
The boy *whose* work is best . . .   The lady to *whom* I have written . . .
The pupil *who* has obtained most marks . . .   The reason *that* I could not come . . .

Who and *whom* usually refer to people; *which* usually refers to things. The rest may refer to either. Remember that these words are only pronouns when they stand by themselves, *not* when they are describing a noun.

Demonstrative pronouns point things out:—
E.g. *These* are mine but *those* are yours. (Notice the possessive pronouns as well!)
I would never do *that*. *This* is not the best way to do it.

A reflexive pronoun refers back to something already mentioned:—
E.g. He killed *himself*.   I saw *myself* in the mirror.   Miss Smith smiled to *herself*.

Emphatic pronouns have the same forms:—
E.g. I *myself* will lead the advance.   Angela, *herself*, was not present at the time.

(a) Write out this passage, and underline all the PERSONAL pronouns:—

I do not think you are working hard enough. Mr Sanders and I are both dissatisfied. We have seen your latest efforts and they are not good enough. It will not do, young man. I have already spoken to your mother about it, and told her what we think. She intends to tell your father, so you will soon be hearing from him as well. We have no doubt that they will want to come and see us, and when we do see them you can expect that you will be in real trouble!

(20)

(b) Replace the words underlined with POSSESSIVE pronouns:—

This is my book. Oh no it's not, it's my property. Well, I say it's not your book at all. What does Tim say? He says that its his book. Oh, and I suppose that Mary says its her book, and that Tom, Dick and Harry all say that it's their book. Don't be silly. How could a book be the property of those three? — Do you still say it's your book, or will you settle for a compromise and call it our book? — It's too late for that; the dog says it's its book, and it's eaten it . . .

(20 — 2 each)

(c) Insert the RELATIVE pronoun which fits best in the gaps marked by asterisks (*):—

(1)   Are you the girl (*) pen was lost?
(2)   I was not sure to (*) I should write.
(3)   The fire brigade rescued the cat (*) was stuck up the tree.
(4)   She's the one (*) did it.
(5)   The decision (*) was made cannot be reversed.
(6)   This is the cat (*) killed the rat!
(7)   Chaudry is a fellow (*) can always be relied on.
(8)   I confronted the man (*) I was supposed to kill.
(9)   I cannot decide (*) work is worse, John's or William's.
(10) The detective, (*) had been listening intently, raised his eyebrows at this.

(20 — 2 each)

(d) Write out this passage and underline (i) the demonstrative pronouns, and (ii) the interrogative pronouns. Put in brackets after each whether it is demonstrative or interrogative. (There are six demonstrative and four interrogative pronouns. Remember: a pronoun must stand by itself, without a noun.)

"Whose is this?" asked the teacher, holding up a book.
"It isn't mine, Miss," said Jane.
"What did you say, Miss?" called out Edward.
"I said, 'Is that yours?' " came the answer.
"Which of them?" said Susan.
"To whom was I talking?" asked Miss icily.
"Don't you know, Miss?" answered Susan with a frown. "That is odd."
"Do these belong to anyone here?" demanded the teacher, even more annoyed.
"Oh, those," answered Ian. "They're mine."
"Then why didn't you say so?" demanded Miss, menacingly.
"I thought you meant these, Miss," said Ian. And Miss gave a strangled cry, — then strangled Ian . . .

(20, 2 each correctly allocated)

FACTSHEET TWELVE

ADJECTIVES

AN ADJECTIVE IS A DESCRIBING WORD. IT DESCRIBES A NOUN.

It adds something to the meaning of the noun. Examples of adjectives are:—
long, wet, happy, hard, silent, empty, painful, remarkable, unknown, suspicious, honest . . .

Adjectives usually go IN FRONT OF the noun, or BETWEEN THE ARTICLE AND ITS NOUN.

If you want to check whether a word is noun or not, put one of the articles in front of it.

If you want to check whether a word is an adjective or not, try putting it in front of a noun, or better still, put it between an article and its noun:—
clever girls; a *silly* mistake; an *unusual* experience; the *new* carpet; *grey* trousers; the *only* hope; the *last* survivors.

Of course you can have two adjectives with a noun:—
all clever girls; *some silly* mistakes; a *new Persian* carpet; *grey short* trousers.

You can also have two adjectives joined by AND in front of a noun:—
silly and unnecessary mistakes; a *striking and unusual* design.

You can have three or more adjectives with a noun.
In this case the last two adjectives of the list are usually joined by AND; other adjectives in a list are separated by COMMAS:—
A *new, blue, Persian* carpet; *silly, lazy and ill-behaved* pupils.
Long, silvery, gleaming and silent missiles; a *new, exciting and novel* plan.
Notice the 'compound adjective' *ill-behaved*. This adjective is made up of two words joined by a hyphen (a little dash). Here are a few other examples:—
strong-willed, new-found, snow-capped, empty-headed.

Adjectives are also found separated from the nouns they describe by a word of *being*, — like *is, was, are, were, have been, used to be* — and others. (This is sometimes known as the 'predicative' use of adjectives.)
For example:— The sensible girls; the girls may be sensible; the girls who are sensible; if the girls are sensible; Are the girls sensible? Will these girls ever be sensible?
When an adjective is used to describe a noun, it is said to *qualify* that noun. In each of the above examples the adjective *sensible* qualifies the noun *girls*. Yet in all but the first example, the adjective is not placed in front of its noun; all the other uses are 'predicative', — but just the same *sensible* still qualifies *girls* each time.

Look at these sentences. The adjectives are all in italics (slanting type):—
The *faint* light of an *early* dawn flecked the *grey* clouds with *pale* streaks of colour.
Despite a *quick* start, the *down* express, hauled by a *large, blue, diesel* locomotive, was brought to a *sudden* halt, when an axle which was *faulty* overheated.
Though John is *clever* he is not *hard-working,* and *all his* work suffers from *constant* inattention and a *poor* attitude.
(Notice that *all* is not directly in front of the noun it qualifies (work).)
Most worksheets are *easy,* but *this* one is *hard.*
Boys who are *keen* and *active* in football are not always *sensible* or *well-behaved* in lessons.
Mrs Warner's qualifications were *ideal* for the *senior* position in the *new* nursery.

(a) Sort these words into two lists: (i) nouns, and (ii) adjectives:—

chair new sausage unusual philosophy vision descriptive reduction unique journey late
unlikely sight spot fashionable huge picture impossible England strong angry swarm ready
engine horrible herd dress arrangement joy Scottish

                                                                                    (15 — ½ each)

(b) Write out these sentences and underline all the adjectives:—
(1)   There is a new boy in the class.
(2)   That is a rare sight.
(3)   Red sky at night, shepherds' delight.
(4)   I am pleased with your homework, Sharon.
(5)   All these sums are wrong, Mark.
(6)   The light was so bright that I could not see.
(7)   Glorious things of thee are spoken.
(8)   Theft is a serious matter.
(9)   Television is a major influence on children's lives.
(10) This is quite an easy exercise.

                                                                                    (10)

(c) Do the same with these. There are two adjectives in each sentence.
(1)   Let us now welcome our distinguished visitor to this auspicious occasion.
(2)   Miss Steel's unswerving devotion to duty is worthy of our commendation.
(3)   All pupils due to go swimming, report to the minibus after lunch.
(4)   Timothy's halting excuses were met with a stony silence.
(5)   Cut-price cabbages for sale here! The best buy in town!

                                                                     (15 — 1½ per adjective)

(d) Insert an adjective that makes good sense into the spaces. Underline the words inserted.
(1)   The................breeze made the................stranger shiver as he walked down the................street of
      the town.
(2)   I approached the................door of the................castle and struck the................shield hung on
      the................portcullis with my lance.
(3)   The................boys who are................for the................window will have to pay for it out of their
      ....money.
(4)   The................meeting of the council to discuss the................rise in the rates produced a................
      and................debate.
(5)   Our fears for the success of the................project proved................when a ....
      report was received from Mrs Wright, our most................executive.
                                                                     (20 — 1 per adjective)

(e) Insert an adjective in front of EVERY noun in these sentences:—
(1)   Boys love food.
(2)   We could just see the castle through the mist.
(3)   The cries of the bats echoed above us.
(4)   Our visit to the museum was most enjoyable.
(5)   It was a sight that now met our eyes.

                                                                     (10 — 1 per adjective)

FACTSHEET THIRTEEN

TYPES OF ADJECTIVES

There are three sorts of adjectives:—

(i) **ADJECTIVES OF QUALITY**

These are simply words that describe.
They answer the question WHAT KIND OF?

E.g. The *angry* man shouted at the *naughty* boy:—
What kind of man — angry; what kind of boy — naughty.
'Angry' and 'naughty' are adjectives of quality.

Other examples:— good, happy, old, blue, serious, cheerful, complete, English, majestic, straight.

(ii) **ADJECTIVES OF QUANTITY**

These give an idea of the number or amount.
They answer the questions HOW MUCH or HOW MANY?
It may be a definite number involved, or it may be a more vague quantity.

E.g. *Both* girls gained *ten* marks in the *first* exercise.
How many girls? — both (which means two); how many marks? — ten; how many exercises involved? — the first (which means one).

All girls gained *many* marks in *some* exercises.

Here 'all', 'many', and 'some' still tell you the quantities, but they are not so precise. (They are sometimes called *indefinite*).

Other examples:— one, twenty, third, double, twenty-seventh (definite);
any, few, several, much, most (indefinite).

Note:— 'a lot of' is not any sort of adjective; it is just poor English; try not to use it. Notice also that the numbers *standing by themselves* are nouns.

(iii) **ADJECTIVES OF DISTINCTION**

These mark off a noun from other nouns of its kind.
(a) Some are called DEMONSTRATIVE
They answer the questions WHICH or WHAT?
E.g. *This* book is yours:— Which book? — The one here, not the one there!

The main demonstrative adjectives are THIS and THAT (singular); THESE and THOSE (plural).
Remember, they are only adjectives with a noun; by themselves, they are pronouns.
Note:— Sometimes the three articles THE, A, AN are counted as this sort of adjective.

(b) Some of them are POSSESSIVE
They answer the question WHOSE?

i.e. *My* friend, *your* pencil case, *his* house, *her* book, *our* car, *their* plans, *its* tail.
Note:— You have already met the possessive PRONOUNS. Remember, a pronoun stands by itself; an adjective qualifies a noun. For example, — It is *mine* (pronoun); it is *my* book (adjective). Which is *his* house? (adjective); Which house is *his*? (pronoun).

(c) Some of them are INTERROGATIVE
These are the words which actually ask the questions:—

i.e. *Which* boy broke the window? *Whose* pullover is this? *What* name shall I put?

Notice that they go in front of a noun, — unlike the interrogative pronouns, which stand by themselves. (*Which* is it? (pronoun). *Which* book is it? (adjective).)

In all these types of adjective remember that an adjective qualifies a noun. If there is no noun around, you probably have a pronoun, not an adjective at all!

(a) What *kind* of chair are you sitting on?

Write down *five* adjectives of QUALITY to describe it.

How many people are in the room (or in the house)?

Write down *five* adjectives of QUANTITY (definite or indefinite) to describe the number.

(10)

(b) Write down all the adjectives of QUANTITY in this passage. (There are twenty).

Both teams played well in the second half. Despite United's first half lead, their new keeper now let in three goals, — though the third goal was an unlucky deflection from the crossbar. This was a double misfortune as he had already saved several far more dangerous shots. The first two goals, however, scored in the tenth and twenty-third minutes of the half, did not leave any doubt in the minds of most of the fans as to which was the better team. Nevertheless, neither side would give up, and United did recover one more goal, bringing the difference down to a single goal only. I still felt that it could go either way, and the few fans who left early missed some real excitement in the last minute, with a triple attack from United's two top strikers, Steel and Mackie, only being held off by some brilliant goalkeeping from Reilly.

(Sounds a good game, doesn't it . . . ?)

(20)

(c) Here is a little play. Underline the adjectives of DISTINCTION in it:—

MUM   Who was that man at the door, Peter?

PETER   What man?

MUM   The one with those silly tricks.

PETER   Do you mean these things?

MUM   (surprised) Which things? — Oh! Yes! Why have you got them?

PETER   (earnestly) I bought them. Those toys there are for Jane, and that gun is for me, and these puzzles are for dad; — oh, and this wooden spoon is for you.

MUM   (exasperated) Look here, that is not your gun, and it's not my spoon. You have to *pay* for these things.

PETER   (slowly) I did. They are all our property. Can I give Jane her toys? — Oh, and the dog its rubber bone? I should think they will both be pleased with their presents.

MUM   (menacingly) If you bought them, whose money did you use?

PETER   (casually) What money? He didn't want any money. — He let me trade in our old car.

MUM   (with a strangled cry) Perhaps you had better give me that wooden spoon, Peter . . .

(20)

(d) In front of *each* of the nouns in this exercise insert TWO adjectives of QUALITY — to improve the story and make it more interesting and exciting. (You can put *and* or *but* between the adjectives.) There are twenty nouns (not counting gas-meter).

The knight reined in his steed before the gate of the castle. From a window above he saw a light flickering in the gloom. The portcullis was half raised. He dismounted and squeezed beneath the bars of iron. With his sword in his hand, he climbed the stairway round the tower. Cautiously he entered the room high in the castle. Before him was the maiden, sat on a chair, gazing out of the window. Slowly she turned to face him. She was not young, — or beautiful, — or even slim. For a moment he gazed on her face. Then he said:— "I've just come to read the gas-meter, madam . . ."

(20 — ½ each)

FACTSHEET FOURTEEN

NOUNS AND ADJECTIVES — (1)

A noun can (nearly always) be *used* as an adjective. This is done simply by placing it in front of another noun (i.e in the place where an adjective would go). Since it now describes (or qualifies) that noun, it is now acting as an adjective.

E.g. Let's go to the *country* today (NOUN): I stayed in a *country* pub (ADJECTIVE).
The rocket sped through *space* (NOUN): *Space* flight is now possible (ADJECTIVE).
In case of *fire*, break the glass (NOUN): The *fire*-doors will close at once (ADJECTIVE).

Many such adjective-noun links have become permanent combinations:— compound nouns.

E.g. *Seahorse, chimney-pot, armchair, cupboard* (originally a board for cups!)

A noun will often have a corresponding adjective.
Many adjectives can be formed from nouns. This is particularly true of abstract nouns.

These adjectives are formed by adding one of many *endings* to the noun, — but the spelling is often changed in the process. You will see this from the following examples:—

IC   angel — angelic; hero — heroic; *but* volcano — volcanic; energy — energetic; type — typical.
       Notice: history makes historic (meaning *important, memorable*), and also historical (meaning *recorded in history*).

Y   fault — faulty; noise — noisy; anger — angry; fire — fiery (note this spelling!)
       Some words add ARY:— custom — customary.

LY   friend — friendly; year — yearly.

OUS   This is very common, but the spelling often changes as well. Danger — dangerous; courage — courageous; mystery — mysterious; mischief — mischievous.

FUL   This is also very common. but remember, only one 'L' — not '-full'. Hate — hateful; harm — harmful; beauty — beautiful; mercy — merciful.
       Notice: Adjectives ending in -ful, often have opposites ending in -less;
       e.g. faithful/faithless; helpful/helpless (not exact opposites in this case).

ABLE or IBLE   Credit — creditable; value — valuable; *but* sense — sensible; terror — terrible.

AL   Continent — continental; industry — industrial; centre — central.
       Notice that there are also words which add IC and AL, like magical.

ISH   Fool — foolish; boy — boyish.

EN   Gold, wool and wood produce golden, woollen and wooden — but often the nouns themselves are used as adjectives. (So 'a gold ring' and 'a golden ring' mean the same thing.)
       There are also, with slighty different meanings, woolly and woody; while silver (noun) makes silver (adjective) and silvery.

ERN   North (noun) produces northern (adjective) or north (adjective); the other compass points work in the same way.

There are many 'endings' which are added to nouns (usually abstract nouns) to turn them into adjectives (usually adjectives of quality). Here are some other examples:—

Fortune — fortunate; quarrel — quarrelsome; rag — ragged; war — warlike;

picture — picturesque; line — linear or lined.

NUMBERS:— The numbers by themselves are NOUNS:— Six (noun) plus five (noun) equals eleven (noun).
                But when they are used to describe a noun, they are adjectives:— I want six (adjective) bananas and five (adjective) apples.
                The numbers that tell you order (first, fifth etc.) can also be both.

Finally there are what might be called PROPER ADJECTIVES:— These are describing words made from proper nouns, like places, countries, etc. They keep their capital letter. Many of them end in -ISH, -SH, or -CH; or -AN.
England — English; Wales — Welsh; France — French; Italy — Italian; India — Indian.
There are also some amusing adjectives formed from city names:—
Glaswegian from Glasgow, Liverpudlian from Liverpool.
They can even be formed from people's names:— Shakespearian = 'to do with Shakespeare', and Dickensian means 'like the books, or characters, or descriptions of Charles Dickens'.

(a) Copy these sentences and at the end of each write down whether the word underlined is being used as a noun or as an adjective.
  1.a. This is a pleasant <u>place</u>.
  1.b. I read a book on English <u>place</u> names today.
  2.a. He lived in the <u>village</u> of Ambridge.
  2.b. The cart rolled slowly down the <u>village</u> street.
  3.a. The old man leaned on his <u>gate</u> post.
  3.b. The <u>gate</u> swung in the breeze.
  4.a. The <u>flower</u>-pots were full of geraniums.
  4.b. The geranium is my favourite <u>flower</u>.
  5.a. The <u>book</u>-case concealed a secret passage.
  5.b. Open the <u>book</u> at page twelve.

                                                                                    (10)

(b) Here are five words which are normally nouns. Use each in a sentence, first as a noun, but secondly as an adjective. After each sentence write clearly NOUN or ADJECTIVE.
  (i) city   (ii) fire   (iii) passenger   (iv) home   (v) school.

                                                                                    (10)

(c) Make each of these nouns into an adjective. You have been told the ending you will need to put on the word, — but be careful! You may well have to change some spelling.
  (1) athlete   (IC)   (4) craft   (Y)   (7) anxiety   (OUS)   (10) grace   (FUL)
  (2) autumn   (AL)   (5) fashion (ABLE)   (8) girl   (ISH)
  (3) silk   (EN)   (6) east   (ERN)   (9) wretch   (ED)

                                                                                    (10)

(d) Make each of these nouns into an adjective. This time you will have to choose the right ending. (For example, — *Peace* becomes *peaceful*).
  (1) winter   (5) colony   (9) spirit   (13) poison   (17) star
  (2) year   (6) force   (10) shadow   (14) pity   (18) youth
  (3) trouble   (7) noise   (11) man   (15) neglect   (19) child
  (4) law   (8) statue   (12) example   (16) energy   (20) giant
                                                                    (10 — ½ each)

(e) Write down the noun from which each of these adjectives derives.
  (For example, — *Metallic* derives from *metal*).
  (1) luxurious   (5) perilous   (9) criminal   (13) fortunate   (17) tattered
  (2) oaken   (6) natural   (10) fiery   (14) laughable   (18) witty
  (3) third   (7) cowardly   (11) elfin   (15) sympathetic (19) merciful
  (4) scientific (8) biblical   (12) manly   (16) systematic (20) splendid
                                                                    (10 — ½ each)

(f) Make each of these nouns into an adjective:—
  (1) fault   (3) poet   (5) grace   (7) impression   (9) point
  (2) mystery   (4) perception (6) might   (8) compassion   (10) favour

                                                                                    (10)

(g) Now use each of the above nouns in a sentence to show its *meaning*.

                                                                                    (10)

(h) Now use each of the adjectives you made for exercise (f) in a sentence to show its *meaning*.

                                                                                    (10)

FACTSHEET FIFTEEN

NOUNS AND ADJECTIVES — (2)

As we have now seen, many adjectives are formed from nouns. This also works the other way round. Many nouns are formed from adjectives. In particular, abstract nouns are very often formed from adjectives of quality. Once again, this is usually done by adding an ENDING.

NESS This is by far the most common ending by which an adjective of quality is turned into an abstract noun. But beware! In the many cases where another ending is used it is wrong to use NESS instead. (So do not write *absentness, confidentness* or *cruelness*.)

Here are some of the other common endings of these abstract nouns:—

TY   CY   ENCE   ANCE   MENT   DOM   HOOD   ICE   TH

Here are some common pairs of Adjectives of Quality and their corresponding Abstract Nouns:—

ADJECTIVE	ABSTRACT NOUN	ADJECTIVE	ABSTRACT NOUN
bright	brightness	constant	constancy
clean	cleanness/cleanliness	accurate	accuracy
dark	darkness	patient	patience
great	greatness	absent	absence
holy	holiness	confident	confidence
like	likeness	distant	distance
ready	readiness	content	contentment
sad	sadness	wise	wisdom
cruel	cruelty	false	falsehood
vain	vanity	just	justice
able	ability	long	length
curious	curiosity	strong	strength
equal	equality	true	truth
fierce	ferocity/fierceness	wide	width
loyal	loyalty	high	height
moral	morality		
real	reality		
secure	security		
simple	simplicity		
gay	gaiety	live (or alive)	life
brave	bravery	hot	heat
indigant	indignation	proud	pride

The last few words in the list are more like pairs of words. There are one or two other very common words of this sort:—

Here are some sentences to show you the use of similar abstract nouns and adjectives of quality:—

Douglas is an *able* boy.   Douglas shows *ability*.

The *ferocity* of the enemy was visible to us all.   We could all see how *fierce* the enemy were.

A *wise* person is never *proud*.   A person of *wisdom* never shows *pride*.

Health and *wealth* are essential to *life* today.   Being *healthy* and *wealthy* are essential to being *alive* today.

I prefer *death* to *dishonour*.   I would rather be *dead* than *dishonourable*.

In the first two exercises, write down the adjective which 'goes with' the noun you have been given. (Most of the nouns are abstract; the adjectives will be adjectives of quality.)

(a)   (1) anger   (3) vanity   (5) justice   (7) equality   (9) length

      (2) truth   (4) pride   (6) fool   (8) noise   (10) angel

(10)

(b)   (1) hideousness   (3) mercy   (5) emotion   (7) quarrel   (9) anxiety

      (2) courage   (4) vanity   (6) absence   (8) constancy   (10) dishonour

(10)

In the second two exercises, write down the noun which 'goes with' the adjective you have been given.

(c)   (1) able   (3) contented   (5) insecure   (7) licentious   (9) great

      (2) happy   (4) high   (6) immoral   (8) alive   (10) joyful

(10)

(d)   (1) loyal   (3) hostile   (5) just   (7) mischievous   (9) various

      (2) rare   (4) late   (6) silly   (8) infectious   (10) cruel

(10)

(e)   In this exercise, correct the incorrect abstract nouns:—

      (1) expandingness   (4) wiseness   (7) eccentricness   (10) readyness

      (2) ferociousness   (5) fireyness   (8) sympatheticness

      (3) erroneousness   (6) indignantness   (9) perilousness

(10)

(f)   Look at the examples at the bottom of the page on the Factsheet. You will see how a sentence can often be written in two different ways, one using an adjective of quality, the other using an abstract noun. Now try to re-write these sentences, replacing an abstract noun with an adjective of quality. You will need to make other changes too.

      (1) Alison shows intelligence.   (6) Douglas is far too prone to mischief.

      (2) Patrick has great strength.   (7) The criminal's story was full of falsehoods.

      (3) I cannot bear disgrace.   (8) I could not believe in the alien's reality.

      (4) His words roused my anger.   (9) The width of the stream is ten metres.

      (5) Curiosity killed the cat!   (10) Loneliness is hard to endure.

(15 — 1½ each)

(g)   In this exercise, do the opposite. Re-write, using an abstract noun instead of an adjective of quality. Once again, you will need to make other changes too.

      (1) Alison is highly intelligent.   (4) The patient was feverish.

      (2) Nancy is rarely silent.   (5) A very fortunate event has occurred.

      (3) She is very like her mother.   (6) A dark cloud overshadowed the sky.

      (7) Being dead is the only sure way of being happy. (TWO to change here!)

      (8) Stupid people are ever vain. (TWO to change again).

(15 — 1½ each)

FACTSHEET SIXTEEN

VERBS

A verb is a DOING WORD. It states an action taking place.

First thing to beware:— it is NOT the name of an action. That would be a naming word, a noun:— *allowance, election, decision, extraction, creation*:— these are all abstract nouns, NOT VERBS.

Here is an assortment of verbs:—
Run, fly, do, try, laugh, shout, arrange, elect, decide, create, destroy, allow, renew, reply, confuse, collapse, constrain, attract, deposit, emphasize, endure, emit, pacify, expand, assign, watch, see, wait, depose, cut, collect, mystify, persuade, frighten, detract, insert, recognise, deduce, put, endure, damage, end.

Second thing to beware:— Some words can be a noun, or a verb, or an adjective. The part of speech depends on the job the word is doing in the sentence. The verb is always the DOING WORD.

The correct way to state a verb is in the infinitive. Here are some verbs in the infinitive:— *to do, to run, to cry, to choose, to arrange, to allow, to destroy.* If you are asked to write down the verbs in a passage, or to give examples of verbs, always give them in the infinitive.

(Note — A good way of checking if something is a verb is to put it into the infinitive; if it is an abstract noun for example, the result will soon show you. 'To allowance', 'To decision', etc., do not make sense).

The person or thing DOING the action of the verb can be a NOUN, or a PRONOUN. The person doing the action of the verb is known as the SUBJECT of the verb, or the SUBJECT of the sentence.

E.g. The boy runs.   Subject: the boy,   Verb: runs.
      He shouts.   Subject: he (pronoun),   Verb: shouts.

Here is a verb written out with all the personal pronouns to show the different persons who might be carrying out the action:—

First person singular:	*I*	*talk*	The FIRST person is the one who is speaking or writing. It may be one person (I) or more than one (WE).
Second person singular:	*You*	*talk*	
Third person singular:	*He*	*talks*	The SECOND person is the one being spoken or written to. It may be one person or several people (but in either case it is YOU).
Third person singular:	*She*	*talks*	
Third person singular:	*It*	*talks*	The THIRD person is anyone else! It may be a HE or a SHE or an IT; or if it is plural it will be THEY.
First person plural:	*We*	*talk*	
Second person plural:	*You*	*talk*	ALL NOUN SUBJECTS ARE THIRD PERSON.
Third person plural:	*They*	*talk*	*NOTICE:*— The verb changes its ending for the third person singular (HE, SHE, IT) *only*.

To make sure you have understood write out a few verbs as above.

Putting a personal pronoun in front of a word you think may be a verb is an even better way of checking it!

(a) Underline all the verbs in these sentences. Notice that some have more than one.
    (1)   I thought I saw a pussy cat. (2)
    (2)   The creature saw me, and slowly approached. (2)
    (3)   The boy ran down the street and round the corner.
    (4)   Round and round he raced, cornered quickly and then started to climb the hill. (4)
    (5)   "Sing me a simple song, sonny," said soppy Sarah. (2)
    (6)   Watch the door while I crawl round behind them, partner. (2)
    (7)   The saints all silent stood in serried ranks around the holy throne.
    (8)   "Who calls my name from yonder bloodstained host?"
    (9)   Down dale and over mountain the valiant band goes on; they do not heed the rain or snow; the noonday sun blazes upon them, but they never faint. (4)
    (10) What answer have you put for number one?

                                                          (20 — 1 per verb)

(b) From this list, select *all* the words that *could be* verbs. (Some of them no doubt could also be nouns or adjectives as well; include these in your list).

thought	arrangement	enslave	polite	subtract	eliminate	flight
tasty	unknown	folder	illuminate	packet	post	dance
turtle	lean	Tasmania	French	translate	rug	make
positive	hysterical	midget	microscope	place	treat	darken
also	mystery	fling	hall	shop	catch	ring
photograph	claim	collapse	deign	magnify	amaze	light
noun	verb	she	fly	face	help	none
choice	management	pride	combine	twenty	slice	all

                                                                        (30)

(c) Use each of these words in a sentence as a VERB. (Beware, they can all also be other parts of speech.)
    (1) fly   (3) journey   (5) train   (7) light   (9) call
    (2) torture (4) slice   (6) wait   (8) ease   (10) pride

                                                                          (10)

(d) Give the persons of the following verbs, with the personal pronouns, as instructed:—
    (1) 1st. person sing. SEE   (4) 2nd. person plur. ARRANGE   (7) 1st. person plur. DO
    (2) 2nd. person sing. ENJOY   (5) 1st. person plur. FLY   (8) *infinitive* of TALK
    (3) 3rd. person plur. CHOOSE   (6) 3rd. person sing. CRY (There are *three* answers!)

                                                                          (10)

(e) Write down the words in this list that CANNOT be verbs:—
Terrify endure master open seat entomb mitigate signify place tie waste eliminate electrify finger

hand trust entrust view photograph blot strike match file crown switch display flee shoe sight site

raise rise storm pen top scamper wriggle turn fast last slow low lower sting hire link chain comb

handle lever hammer speed voyage endure meet change distress anger snare drug engineer peg

                                                             (10 — subtract one for each mistake)

FACTSHEET SEVENTEEN

THE PRESENT TENSE OF VERBS

Every verb in English has several TENSES. The tense of a verb tells you the TIME when the action occurred. The examples given on the first factsheet were in the PRESENT TENSE. The present tense is the tense of actions happening NOW, in the present, at this moment.

(Did you notice that NOT all the examples on the worksheet you have just done were in the present tense?)

You have already seen one verb in the present tense written out in full:—

I talk: you talk: he/she/it talks: we talk: you talk: they talk.

This can be called the SIMPLE present tense. There are also COMPOUND present tenses:—

I am talking: you are talking: he/she/it is talking: we are talking: you are talking: they are talking.

This one is called the CONTINUOUS present tense. It gives the idea of the action carrying on for a while.

Here is another compound present tense:—

I do talk: you do talk: he/she/it does talk: we do talk: you do talk: they do talk.

This one is called the EMPHATIC present tense. It is used to stress or emphasise what is being done. ("You *do* misbehave, Mark" . . . "They *do* want to go really" . . .)

All these three forms are ways of saying that someone is carrying out a particular action at the present.

The CONTINUOUS and EMPHATIC present tenses have another very important use in English. They are the only forms of the present tense that can be used in the NEGATIVE — i.e. when you want to say that something is NOT happening.

You cannot say *I talk not* or *you talk not.*
In Old English you could say this, but it is no longer used.

Instead you have to say:
I do not talk . . . You do not talk   or   *I am not talking . . . You are not talking.*

Look at the forms of the present tense written out for comparison:—

SIMPLE		CONTINUOUS			EMPHATIC		
I	talk	I	am	talking	I	do	talk
You	talk	You	are	talking	You	do	talk
He	talks	He	is	talking	He	does	talk
She	talks	She	is	talking	She	does	talk
It	talks	It	is	talking	It	does	talk
We	talk	We	are	talking	We	do	talk
You	talk	You	are	talking	You	do	talk
They	talk	They	are	talking	They	do	talk

These are all POSITIVE forms of the verb. They state an action which does actually happen.

You will often in the compound tenses find other words inserted between the parts of the verb:—

It may simply be NOT to make the negative:— I *do* NOT *go;* he *does* NOT *talk;* they *are* NOT *going.*

It may be other words:— he *does* not often *talk;* we *are* always *trying;* she *is* eventually *coming;* I *am* slowly but surely *understanding.*

34

(80)

(a) Give the persons of the following verbs in the SIMPLE PRESENT tense:—

    (1)   2nd person plur. DECIDE

    (2)   3rd person plur. TRUST

    (3)   1st person plur. CHOOSE

    (4)   Infinitive of SHOW

    (5)   1st person sing. ELECT

    (6)   2nd person sing. HELP

    (7)   2nd person plur. JUMP

    (8)   3rd person sing. DIE (3 answers)

    (10)

(b) In these sentences the verbs are in the simple form of the present tense. Rewrite them using the *continuous* present tense ('I am talking' etc.)

    (1)   Tina always talks.

    (2)   The Girls misbehave in class.

    (3)   Catherine works very hard.

    (4)   We write as neatly as possible.

    (5)   My father does the cooking in our house.

    (6)   The light shines dimly upon the gloomy castle.

    (7)   The grey dawn breaks upon the desolate beach.

    (8)   The sun rises hesitantly into a sky of scudding clouds.

    (9)   Out of the lapping waves a mighty form silently arises.

    (10)   The great beast gazes upon the small form tied to the jagged rocks.

    (20 — 2 each)

(c) Put these sentences into the negative using the emphatic version of the present tense with do/does. You may need to change the order of some of the other words.

    (1)   The enemy shell us constantly.

    (2)   The shot lands nearby.

    (3)   Our men hurry to take cover.

    (4)   The captain decides upon an advance.

    (5)   Our troops soon reach the enemy lines.

    (6)   They easily storm the ramparts.

    (7)   Fighting courageously, our forces manage to sieze enemy headquarters.

    (8)   Now we see our flag floating over their lines.

    (9)   We suffer few casualties.

    (10)   Our men are returning to base in good order.

    (20 — 2 each)

(d) Put these sentences into the positive, using the SIMPLE form of the present tense:—

    (1)   James is not working to the best of his ability.

    (2)   Surely Steve is not playing about at the back of the class.

    (3)   Stuart does not join in the class's misbehaviour.

    (4)   The other boys do not like him.

    (5)   Upon the arrival of the teacher they do not continue in this opinion.

    (6)   The girls are not singing sweetly today.

    (7)   The sound of their voices really does not deafen me.

    (8)   I am not getting a headache.

    (9)   I do not need to take an aspirin.

    (10)   I am not suffering from perforated eardrums.

    (20 — 2 each)

(e) Change the verbs in these sentences from the singular to the plural. Keep the same person, but use that person in the plural not the singular. If the subject is a noun you will need to make it plural. You may find you need to make some other changes.

    (1)   I am going out today.

    (2)   The soldier shoots him.

    (3)   She calls her son repeatedly.

    (4)   Now you know the answer.

    (5)   I love playing football.

    (6)   He always plays about in lessons.

    (7)   You see the stars through the clouds.

    (8)   You are taking a serious risk.

    (9)   It is eating its bone in the garden.

    (10)   The light is shining brightly now.

    (10)

FACTSHEET EIGHTEEN

VERBS — QUESTIONS AND ORDERS

You have already seen that the compound present tenses are used to make the negative:— I AM NOT GOING/I DO NOT GO.

They are also used to make the INTERROGATIVE (the form used for asking questions). The interrogative is formed by reversing the order of subject and the first part of the verb, — with or without a question word in front. This sounds more complicated than it is.

YOU ARE GOING becomes ARE YOU GOING? (or 'Why are you going?'/'When are you going?' etc.) We cannot say TALK-YOU, using the simple form of the verb, but we can, of course, say DO YOU TALK? (or 'Why do you talk?' etc.)

The procedure is the same when the subject is a noun:—

'Mother is feeding the baby' becomes 'Is mother feeding the baby?'
'Tessa likes spaghetti' becomes 'Does Tessa like spaghetti?'

Negative questions work like this:—

Statement: You are going

Question: Are you going?

Negative Question: Are you not going? (usually abbreviated to:— Aren't you going?)

Here are some other examples:— Do you not see? (Don't you see?)
Are the enemy not advancing? (Aren't the enemy advancing?)
Is it not an amusing sight? (Isn't it an amusing sight?)

You may have noticed that negative questions like this expect the person to reply YES. (You can also do this by putting SURELY in front of the question: 'Surely you are coming?') NOTICE:— You can ask a question WITHOUT reversing the verb-subject order:— 'You *are* coming?' However, these usually add a reversed verb at the end:—

'You are coming, aren't you?' 'You do love me, don't you?' The answer expected is YES!

If you want to ask a question expecting the answer NO, put SURELY and NOT in:— 'Surely you are not talking, Ben?' The 'expected' answer is 'no' even though the answer may well be 'yes'.

We have now had two forms of sentence:— THE STATEMENT
THE QUESTION
There is a third:—   THE COMMAND

Commands are normally addressed to a person or group of people (in other words, they refer to the *second* person, singular or plural:— you could put 'Hey, YOU' in front of most commands). Commands use a form of the verb called the IMPERATIVE. It is the same as the YOU form of the present tense, but without the YOU. Here are some examples (from which you will see it is very simple):—

Do it at once, you naughty girl. *Stand* up, Jonathan. *Come* here, the boy who is talking. *Charge* for the guns! *Stop* it! "*Come* into my parlour," said the spider to the fly. *Follow* me, ladies. *Fear* no man, *love* God, *honour* the Emperor!

Since commands are often shouted, they often have an exclamation mark (!)

NEGATIVE COMMANDS are made with the phrase: *do not* (or *don't*) and the verb.

Don't be such a naughty girl. *Don't cry*, Luke. *Do not speak* to me like that! *Do not try* to escape, Mr Bond; all the exits are guarded by my robots.

(a) Make these statements into questions:—

    (1)   She likes English very much.   (3)   We are going swimming this afternoon.

    (2)   There is your stupid pen!   (4)   I see another blot on your book, Kate.

    (5)   We are having sausage and mash for lunch today.

    (6)   Mandy is reading that terrible magazine again.

    (7)   We are to pack up at four o'clock, even if Miss Evans hasn't returned.

    (8)   The rain in Spain falls mainly on the plain.

    (9)   James is either eating a very large banana, or he is growing a long yellow nose. (TWO verbs to change)

        (10)

(b) Make these questions into statements:—

    (1)   Are you on exercise (b) now?   (3)   Can I have another apple?

    (2)   Are we having chips again?   (4)   Is he the boy who broke the window?

    (5)   Are we all going to the beach today instead of lessons?

    (6)   Do you have ten pence to lend me till tomorrow, David?

    (7)   Are they all going to get into trouble now?

    (8)   Does their mother do their homework, or do they get brighter at home? (TWO)

    (9)   Is Elaine really better at maths than her big brother?

        (10)

(c) Make these statements into commands. (Remember, HE, SHE, THEY etc. must become YOU — or disappear altogether.)

    (1)   The boys are standing up.   (3)   Lucy is working hard for the exams.

    (2)   You believe anything!   (4)   Salma is just showing me her exercise book.

    (5)   They are standing to attention when the officer is talking to them.

    (6)   His sweetheart falls into his arms and kisses him passionately . . . (TWO)

    (7)   Oliver is reading that book of love stories again.

    (8)   You walk down towards Trebunnion for seven miles, then you turn left and after half an hour or so at the top of the hill, you take the track signposted 'Soarfoot Twelve' . . .(THREE)

    (9)   "You are talking sense for once, Captain Burbble," said the General.

    (10)   The Guides are now walking up the hill.

    (11)   They are following the trail.

    (12)   The stars are shining, the band is playing, you gaze into my eyes. (THREE)

    (13)   Jack and Jill go up the hill.

    (14)   Michelle stands beside me and watches the children playing in the garden. (TWO)

        (20 — 1 per verb changed)

(d) Turn the statements in exercise (c) into negative questions.

        (20 — 1 per verb changed)

(e) Make these questions into negative commands! (You will need to make *many* changes).

    (1)   Are you cheeking me, young lady?   (5)   Are they writing neatly?

    (2)   Is William behaving himself?   (6)   Are you girls getting your books out?

    (3)   Are you laughing in class, Adam?   (7)   Is it allowed?

    (4)   Is he going to crash?   (8)   Do you spurn me again, my love?

    (9)   Do you rely on the police to protect your property, Mrs Stevenson?

    (10)   Are you trying to annoy John by hiding his ruler, Benjamin?

        (10)

FACTSHEET NINETEEN

WILL AND WAS

You have already done a good deal of work on the PRESENT tense of verbs, — the tense dealing with action happening now, in the present. You have also seen that there are various forms of it, one simple, and some compound.

The next tense we are going to deal with is the FUTURE.

Obviously, this deals with future action. It is a compound tense, and is formed by putting WILL or SHALL in front of the verb. Here is the future tense of a verb written out:—

I	SHALL	GO
YOU	WILL	GO
HE	WILL	GO
SHE	WILL	GO
IT	WILL	GO
WE	SHALL	GO
YOU	WILL	GO
THEY	WILL	GO

NOTICE the forms 'I shall go' and 'we shall go'. For the first person, singular and plural, (the 'I' and 'we' forms) *shall* is the correct form of the future tense.

You *can* write 'I will go' or 'we will go', but these forms give the idea of 'intention' or 'determination' or 'wish' — as well as just a future sense. So, 'I shall drown' means 'Oh dear; I'm about to drown', while 'I will drown' means 'I have decided I am going to drown (and don't try to stop me!)'.

However, since the future tense often includes the idea of intention, it is now very common to see 'I will go' or 'we will go', — and there is not *too* much wrong with it.

Incidentally, if you write things like 'You shall go; he shall go; they shall go' — it is rather like giving an order!

REMINDER:— Nouns are very often the subjects of verbs, as well as the pronouns.

QUESTION:— Why does *you* occur twice? — Check Factsheet Sixteen if you are not sure.

NOTE:— There is also a CONTINUOUS form of the FUTURE:— *I shall be going, You will be going, He/She/It will be going, We shall be going, You will be going, They will be going.*

Now we are going on to the first of the PAST tenses. — There are quite a few of them! — We start with a compound tense, used for continuous action in the past. Its proper name is the IMPERFECT tense (because its action is not finished, — i.e. 'imperfect'!) It is formed by adding -ING to the end of the main verb, and putting WAS or WERE in front. It is the most common form of the verb in the past that we use when we are talking. Here it is written out:—

I	WAS	GOING
YOU	WERE	GOING
HE	WAS	GOING
SHE	WAS	GOING
IT	WAS	GOING
WE	WERE	GOING
YOU	WERE	GOING
THEY	WERE	GOING

People do sometimes make mistakes in using WAS or WERE. Now is the time to learn which is which. (I, he, she, it — followed by *was; we, you, they* — followed by *were*; singular nouns followed by *was*; plural nouns followed by *were*). Normally you can tell if something is right just by reading or saying it aloud. In some *dialects* (variations in the form of English used in different regions or countries) it is quite common to hear "I were going"; — but don't write it (unless you are writing speech in dialect!)

The verbs in both future and imperfect tenses are compound. They are made up of the main verb (the one at the end, which tells you what the action itself is), and the auxiliary verb (auxiliary means 'helper'; the help it provides is to tell you what the tense is).

It is very easy to make these tenses negative:— *I shall not go; You will not die; He was not going; They were not singing.*

It is also easy to make them into questions: *Shall I go? Will he die? Was he going? Were they singing? Shall I not go (or Shan't I go)? Was he not going (or Wasn't he going)?*

38

(a) The following sentences are in the present tense. Re-write them in the *future* tense. (If you think the continuous form of the future is best, use that).

(1)   Louise is always singing.   (4)   I write good English.
(2)   Why is the baby crying?   (5)   That does not make sense.
(3)   Nicola does not like Penny.   (6)   Why are you not listening?
(7)   I am not accepting work of this standard, Johnny.
(8)   Surely you are not writing to that Clive again, Anthea?
(9)   The Chairman is not seeing anyone today, Smith.
(10) I never trust people wearing dark glasses!

                                                                (20 — 2 each)

(b) This exercise is the same sort of thing. The sentences are in the present tense. This time, put them into the *imperfect* tense.

(1)   Are you going to the shops?   (4)   Why is she climbing that ladder?
(2)   The house is being painted.   (5)   What does he do in that shed all day?
(3)   Fang is biting that policeman again.   (6)   She writes to her mother every day.
(7)   Is that the baby crying again, or am I imagining it ? (TWO)
(8)   How do you expect me to concentrate when that awful child is howling all day? (TWO)

                                                                (20 — 2 each)

(c) In these sentences there are mistakes with the verbs that are used (not only with the imperfect and future, but also the present tense). Re-write the sentences, correcting the mistakes:—

(1)   The baby are not crying again, am it? (TWO)
(2)   I never likes people who talks too much. (TWO)
(3)   I were walking down the street, and Lisa were coming along the other way with Clyde. (TWO)
(4)   I will be going to the pictures tonight, Shirley. Shall you be coming with me? (TWO)
(5)   All trains stops at Crewe.
(6)   They was all working quietly.
(7)   I does not see why you is complaining all the time. (TWO)
(8)   We was driving fast, and the houses was rushing by, as the car were eating up the miles. (THREE)
(9)   "We will pass the Odeon soon," Liz were saying. "I will tell you when I sees it." (FOUR)
(10) John, Joanne, Steven and Rose was all coming to the pictures.

                                                          (20 — 1 per verb changed)

(d) Some of the following sentences are in the future, some in the past. Change them around, so that the ones that were future tense become imperfect tense, and the ones that were imperfect become future!

(1)   Were you waiting for me?   (4)   I shall not be singing.
(2)   Where will they go?   (5)   The dogs were barking all night.
(3)   We shall overcome.   (6)   She was leaving on the nine o'clock train.
(7)   We were all hoping for a change of government on Thursday.
(8)   Will you really look for the treasure in Doomrock Caves?
(9)   Mrs Hale, mother and I were going to the theatre.
(10) Who will walk along the cliff path on a windy night?

                                                                (20 — 2 each)

FACTSHEET TWENTY

PAST TENSES

You have seen how one tense in past time, *the imperfect* (for example, 'I was going'), is formed by using an auxiliary verb (was/were) and a form of the main verb ending in -ING ('walking, talking' etc). This form of the verb is called the PRESENT PARTICIPLE. (It is not so odd that it should be the 'present' participle; it is used in the present tense, for example in 'I am walking, he is talking'.)

As well as the imperfect tense, all verbs have several other tenses in past time. Firstly there is a *simple* PAST tense, often just called THE PAST (but correctly known as the AORIST). Here a verb written out in the past (aorist) tense:—

I	TALKED
YOU	TALKED
HE	TALKED
SHE	TALKED
IT	TALKED
WE	TALKED
YOU	TALKED
THEY	TALKED

Most verbs in English make their PAST TENSE by simply adding -ED to the end of the verb.

Because it is a 'simple' tense (no auxiliary verb) there is a problem making the negative and questions. Just as you cannot say TALK-I? or I NOT TALK, so you cannot say TALKED-I? or I NOT TALKED. In the present tense, we had to use a compound form, and the same applies in the past tense.

Do you remember *I do talk; I do not talk; Do I talk?* etc.? Just as in the present we use DO, in the past we use DID. So you get *I did talk* (used for emphasizing or stressing the fact) *I did not talk, he did not shout, we did not walk, did they laugh?* etc.

NOTE:— With the question word *who* you can say *Who talked? Who laughed?* etc.

As well as the aorist, there is a compound tense in past time, known as the PERFECT TENSE ('perfect' because the action is finished, complete, or perfect; in the imperfect it is unfinished!)

The PERFECT TENSE is formed by an auxiliary verb — HAS/HAVE — plus another participle, this time, the PAST PARTICIPLE. It sounds complicated, but for most verbs it is very easy. The past participle for most verbs is exactly the same as the form of the past tense; that is, it is just the ordinary verb with -ED on the end. (So the past participle of *talk* is *talked*.)

Here is the perfect tense written out in full:—

I	HAVE	TALKED
YOU	HAVE	TALKED
HE	HAS	TALKED
SHE	HAS	TALKED
IT	HAS	TALKED
WE	HAVE	TALKED
YOU	HAVE	TALKED
THEY	HAVE	TALKED

Obviously there is no problem in making negatives or questions with this tense:—
Have I talked? Has she called?
He has not talked. They have not decided.

You can also make a CONTINUOUS form of the perfect tense. For this you need an extra auxiliary verb (BEEN), and the present participle instead of the past! It is simpler than it sounds once again though:—
I have been talking, you have been shouting, it has been barking, etc.

You can also get even further into the past, with the PLUPERFECT TENSE. This is in fact very easy. You just use HAD instead of HAS and HAVE.
I had talked, she had shouted, we had waited, etc.

Then you can have a CONTINUOUS form of the pluperfect:—
I had been talking, he had been dreaming, they had been working.

Finally, there is a tense called the FUTURE PERFECT, which is a cross between future and perfect:—
I shall have talked, you will have walked, etc.; and the continuous form: I shall have been talking.

(a) Write out the imperfect, past (simple) and perfect tense equivalents of the following verbs in the present tense. Use the same person as that in the question. (So, for example, if the question says: 'He shouts', you would write: 'He was shouting; he shouted; he has shouted' — in that order).

(1) I talk

(2) She is dancing

(3) They decide

(4) We are painting

(5) You arrange

(6) It does bark

(7) He collects

(8) I am walking

(9) They are voting

(10) She dresses

(30 — 1 for each tense)

(b) These sentences have verbs in the imperfect tense. Rewrite them, changing the tense to past (simple).

(1) Bridget was watching television.

(2) We were waiting on the platform.

(3) I was talking to Julie.

(4) Mum was painting the kitchen.

(5) No, I was not smoking. (Check the Factsheet on how to do the negative in this tense).

(6) Why were you looking at me? (Check the Factsheet on questions).

(7) Who was talking?

(8) My plan was working at last.

(9) While I was watching, the man was scribbling a note in his book. (TWO)

(10)

(c) Re-write all your answers to exercise (b), this time putting all the verbs into the PERFECT tense.

(10)

(d) Make the following sentences NEGATIVE:—

(1) That baby cries a great deal.

(2) Jimmy was swinging on the gate.

(3) The dying man cried aloud.

(4) The sound was echoing in the room.

(5) Kim has proved her value to the team.

(6) The bull charged his vicious tormentor.

(7) You have been listening carefully.

(8) Why did you answer me?

(9) She had been waiting for his arrival.

(10) Have you done your homework?

(10)

(e) The following sentences are all in various forms of the present tense. Re-write each of them with the verb(s) changed into the tense named at the end of each sentence.

(1) Sandra acts quickly to prevent a serious fire in the kitchen. (PAST (simple)).

(2) You are always misbehaving in lessons, Paul. (PLUPERFECT).

(3) The train rushes through the station, although there are passengers waiting. (TWO verbs, first one PAST (simple), second one IMPERFECT).

(4) My pen is leaking, and the ink is flowing onto my book. (TWO — both IMPERFECT).

(5) Jo is frowning as Mr Carter explains the problem. (TWO — IMPERFECT and PAST (simple)).

(6) Who is whispering while I am talking? (TWO — both IMPERFECT).

(7) I do not like chips; I prefer boiled potatoes. (TWO — both PAST (simple)).

(8) The detective questions him, but he refuses to answer. (TWO — PERFECT CONTINUOUS!)

(9) The stranger walks up the road, turns the corner, and then opens the gate. (THREE — all PERFECT).

(10) The engine is clanking and hissing as if it will explode. (THREE — first two PAST (simple), third — IMPERFECT).

(20 — 1 per verb changed)

FACTSHEET TWENTY-ONE

IRREGULAR VERBS

Anyone learning foreign languages will recognise this heading. An irregular verb is one that doesn't behave like most other verbs in the way it forms its tenses. (If you think about the American usage of 'regular' to mean normal or usual, then 'irregular' presumably means unusual). English has plenty of these verbs, and some of them are among the commonest that we use every day.

In English verbs are 'irregular' in the way they form their PAST TENSE (or aorist), and their PAST PARTICIPLE (needed for the perfect tense).

Here is a 'Regular' Verb:
PRESENT   I talk etc.   PAST   I talked etc.   PAST PARTICIPLE   Talked.

But what about: 'I run, I ran, I have run'; or 'I write, I wrote, I have written'? You can't say 'I runned', or 'I have writed'! These verbs are *irregular,* and so are many others. Here is a list of some of them.

PRESENT	PAST TENSE	PAST PARTICIPLE	PRESENT	PAST TENSE	PAST PARTICIPLE
am	was	been	kneel	knelt	knelt
awake	awoke	awakened	know	knew	known
bear	bore	borne	lay	laid	laid
beat	beat	beaten	lead	led	led
begin	began	begun	leave	left	left
bend	bent	bent	lend	lent	lent
bite	bit	bitten	lie	lay	lain
bleed	bled	bled	lose	lost	lost
blow	blew	blown	make	made	made
break	broke	broken	mean	meant	meant
bring	brought	brought	meet	met	met
build	built	built	pay	paid	paid
buy	bought	bought	read	read	read
catch	caught	caught	ride	rode	ridden
choose	chose	chosen	ring	rang	rung
come	came	come	rise	rose	risen
creep	crept	crept	run	ran	run
cut	cut	cut	say	said	said
dig	dug	dug	see	saw	seen
do	did	done	sell	sold	sold
draw	drew	drawn	send	sent	sent
dream	dreamt	dreamt	shake	shook	shaken
	(or dreamed)	(or dreamed)	shoot	shot	shot
drink	drank	drunk	shut	shut	shut
drive	drove	driven	sing	sang	sung
eat	ate	eaten	sink	sank	sunk
fall	fell	fallen	sit	sat	sat
feel	felt	felt	sleep	slept	slept
fight	fought	fought	speak	spoke	spoken
find	found	found	spin	spun or span	spun
fly	flew	flown	stand	stood	stood
forget	forgot	forgotten	stick	stuck	stuck
freeze	froze	frozen	sting	stung	stung
get	got	got	swim	swam	swum
give	gave	given	take	took	taken
go	went	gone	tear	tore	torn
grow	grew	grown	tell	told	told
have	had	had	think	thought	thought
hear	heard	heard	wear	wore	worn
hide	hid	hidden	weave	wove	woven
hurt	hurt	hurt	write	wrote	written
keep	kept	kept			

(a) The following verbs are all given in the present tense. Change them into the PAST (simple).

(1)	I am writing	(9)	You fly	(17)	You mean	(25)	I do not drink
(2)	You make	(10)	He catches	(18)	We are shutting	(26)	You are talking
(3)	He feels	(11)	It starts	(19)	He is selling	(27)	She sleeps
(4)	She is drawing	(12)	She knows	(20)	They wear	(28)	They are not swimming
(5)	We cut	(13)	We ride	(21)	She is shooting	(29)	Are you running?
(6)	You are lying	(14)	You sit	(22)	Who is fighting?	(30)	Aren't they buying?
(7)	They ring	(15)	They eat	(23)	It sinks		
(8)	I am laughing	(16)	I say	(24)	I lead		

(15 — ½ each)

(b) Now do something similar with the verbs in exercise (a), but this time put them into the PERFECT tense (I have talked, I have written etc.)

(15 — ½ each)

(c) Here is a group of verbs that are in the PAST (simple) tense. Change them into the PERFECT tense.

(1)	I met	(6)	She wore	(11)	We rang	(16)	He sent
(2)	You sang	(7)	It stuck	(12)	It shook	(17)	Did he fly?
(3)	He decided	(8)	I slept	(13)	They were	(18)	You did not speak
(4)	They drove	(9)	You built	(14)	I do	(19)	I dreamt (TWO POS-
(5)	We chose	(10)	He hid	(15)	You have		SIBLE ANSWERS)

(10 — ½ each)

(d) This time we reverse the process. Here are some verbs in the PERFECT tense. Change them into the PAST (simple) tense.

(1)	I have spoken	(8)	It has rung	(15)	I have not decided
(2)	You have fallen	(9)	She has left	(16)	Who has seen?
(3)	He has risen	(10)	He has heard	(17)	Where have you been?
(4)	They have met	(11)	It has frozen	(18)	They have not ridden
(5)	We have chosen	(12)	We have waited	(19)	Have you eaten?
(6)	It has departed	(13)	They have sold	(20)	You have known
(7)	She has forgotten	(14)	You have taken		

(10 — ½ each)

(e) In this exercise, the verbs in the sentences may be in any tense. Rewrite the sentences putting the verbs into the tenses written in capitals at the end of each.

(1) Although Mary is working hard, she has not made much progress. (TWO — IMPERFECT and PLUPERFECT)

(2) When it happens, it will go with a bang. (TWO — PERFECT and FUTURE PERFECT)

(3) We made our choice, and we have stuck to it. (TWO — PLUPERFECT and PAST (simple))

(4) I have never liked Miss Wilson, however much Susan praised her. (TWO — FUTURE and PRESENT)

(5) Mark was departing in a huff, but he came back on a bicycle. (TWO — PAST (simple) and PERFECT)

(10 — 1 per verb changed)

(f) Now go through the *original* sentences, and write down for each the tenses of the verbs. (There are two verbs in each sentence).

(10)

FACTSHEET TWENTY-TWO

THE PASSIVE

Look at these sentences:— (a) The man eats the fish.

(b) The fish is being eaten by the man.

In (a) you have a straightforward sentence of the sort you are used to. 'The man' is the subject of the verb. The verb is 'eats'. 'The fish' is the OBJECT of the sentence. The thing which suffers or experiences the action of the verb is known as the OBJECT. In a sense it is the opposite to the subject.

When a verb has an object, it is known as a 'transitive' verb. This means that the action of the verb is 'carried over' to its object. Verbs do not have to have an object. You can say "I am running" and make perfect sense without any object. Verbs with no object are called 'intransitive'.

Now look again at the two sentences. In (b) 'The fish' has become the subject of the sentence. But the verb has changed its form. It is now in what is known as the PASSIVE VOICE. When a verb is in the PASSIVE the action returns to the subject of the verb. 'The fish' is the subject, but the fish is also suffering the action (pretty obviously, since it is being eaten!)

'The man' was the subject in sentence (a); in (b) he is added on at the end as a kind of footnote to tell you by whom the poor old fish is being eaten. 'The man' is the AGENT of the action. We could also have an INSTRUMENT of the action. In this sentence: 'The fish is being eaten by the man *with a fork'*, 'a fork' is the instrument. The agent tells you BY whom the action was done, the instrument tells you WITH what it was done.

The main thing to remember in recognizing a passive verb is to check if the subject is what receives back the action of the verb. There is an obvious difference between 'I punch Tim' (I am doing the punching) and 'I am punched by Tim' (I am the one who is getting punched).

It is fairly easy to change a sentence round from one to the other. 'John's father is calling him'*(active)* means much the same as 'John is being called by his father'*(passive)*.

When the subject simply performs an action, or when the action carries over on to someone or something else, the verb is called ACTIVE. When the action returns to the subject, the verb is called PASSIVE.

The passive is formed using the verb 'to be' as an auxiliary, — as are some of the active tenses. You have already seen many tenses of the verb in the active voice. Here are their equivalent in the passive:—

	ACTIVE	PASSIVE
PRESENT TENSE	I like I am liking (I do like)	I am liked I am being liked
FUTURE TENSE	I shall like (I shall be liking)	I shall be liked
IMPERFECT TENSE	I was liking	I was being liked
PAST TENSE (Simple or Aorist)	I liked (I did like)	I was liked
PERFECT TENSE	I have liked (I have been liking)	I have been liked
PLUPERFECT TENSE	I had liked (I had been liking)	I had been liked
FUTURE PERFECT TENSE	I shall have liked (I shall have been liking)	I shall have been liked

(a) Copy out these sentences, and next to each write ACTIVE or PASSIVE. Remember, the way to check is to see if the action of the verb returns to the subject. (In 'The fish is being eaten', 'The fish' is the subject, but there is also no doubt that it is 'the fish' which is having the eating done to it!)

(1) John is being called.	(11) Our books are being marked by the teacher.
(2) Susan is playing a game.	(12) Have you made your choice yet?
(3) "Dinner is served, My Lord."	(13) Why is Ben being smacked?
(4) I do like fish and chips.	(14) He has just broken the window with a football.
(5) I am writing to Aunt Martha.	(15) The window has been smashed to pieces.
(6) The fish have been caught.	(16) Ben is howling very loudly.
(7) The fish have escaped.	(17) I am being deafened by the noise.
(8) They have broken my net.	(18) Will you sweep up the glass, please?
(9) My best net was broken.	(19) Nothing else has been damaged.
(10) The teacher is marking our books.	(20) Perhaps he will be more careful in future.

(10 — ½ each)

(b) The following sentences are in the ACTIVE voice. Try to rewrite them, changing the verbs into the passive, but keeping the same meaning. — So what was the object will become the subject, and what was the subject will become the agent or instrument. (E.g. 'The man is painting the house' would become 'The house is being painted by the man'.) Try to keep to the same *tense* as the original.

(1) The man is eating the fish.	(11) Sandra has chosen another new boyfriend.
(2) John's father is calling him.	(12) The workmen were unblocking the drains.
(3) Joanne was reading a book.	(13) Paul always displays excellent ball control.
(4) The teacher is marking our books.	(14) Patrick had observed a new star.
(5) Elizabeth won the first race.	(15) A dagger stabbed him through the heart.
(6) Tessa has written a letter.	(16) Mum is buying the new wallpaper.
(7) Kevin's voice deafens me.	(17) Why has she bought that boring pattern?
(8) David scored two goals.	(18) She is hanging it in the hall.
(9) Did mother feed the baby?	(19) The children are providing assistance.
(10) Has anyone fed the baby today?	(20) Perhaps mother will hang the children instead!

(40 — 2 each)

(c) This exercise is the reverse of (b). The sentences are in the passive. Your job is to change them into the active, keeping the same meaning. (E.g. 'The window has been broken by Ben' becomes 'Ben has broken the window'.) Once again, keep the same tense.

(1) The fish is being eaten by the man.	(6) That wardrobe will soon have been eaten by those woodworm.
(2) John is being called by his father.	(7) It was done with a sharp knife.
(3) The house has been painted by me.	(8) Your cooking has been improved by the addition of those spices.
(4) By which bad boy was this drawing done?	
(5) Has your room been hit by a hurricane, Tracy?	(9) The sails were shaken by a gentle breeze.
	(10) Has the design been approved by Valery?

(20 — 2 each)

(d) Finally, to show you have understood the passive, write down five sentences of your own in which the verb is ACTIVE (numbered 1 to 5), and five sentences in which it is PASSIVE (6 to 10).

(10)

FACTSHEET TWENTY-THREE

AUXILIARY VERBS

Now you have seen how all the tenses are formed, both in the active and the passive voice, you have a fair idea about how auxiliary verbs work, so some of this Factsheet will be revision.

Firstly we will look at the verb TO BE.

It is used for the continuous form of the present, for any other continuous forms of tenses, for the imperfect, and for every tense of the passive.

But it can also be perfectly good MAIN verb standing by itself.

In 'I am talking' and 'I was going' and 'It has been painted' *am, was* and *been* are acting as auxiliary verbs, to assist the main verbs, *talk, go* and *paint.*

In 'I am a good boy', 'He was impossible' and 'You have been naughty' the same three parts of the verb TO BE are the main verb of the sentence. (In the last one, the verb TO BE needs its own auxiliary verb, *have,* to form the perfect tense!)

It is easy enough to tell if TO BE is being used as main or auxiliary verb; simply check if it is closely linked with another verb, in which case it is auxiliary; or if it has no other verb linked with it, but is followed by a noun or adjective, in which case it is the main verb.

The verb TO BE is so important it is worth seeing all its tenses written out:—

PRESENT: I am, you are, he/she/it is, we are, you are, they are.

FUTURE: I shall be, you will be, he/she/it will be, we shall be, you will be, they will be.

IMPERFECT: I was being, you were being, he/she/it was being, we were being, you were being, they were being.

PAST (Aorist): I was, you were, he/she/it was, we were, you were, they were.

PERFECT: I have been, you have been, he/she/it has been, we have been, you have been, they have been.

PLUPERFECT: I had been, etc.   FUTURE PERFECT: I shall have been, etc.

(The verb to be has no passive: 'I am been' wouldn't make much sense!)

You have also already seen the use of HAVE and HAS to make the perfect tense, and HAD to make the pluperfect. They can also stand by themselves as MAIN verbs, e.g. in 'I have a bad cold', 'I had a new book', 'I have had measles'. (In the last one *have* is auxiliary to *had*!)

Then there are DO and DID to make 'emphatic' forms of the present and past, but more importantly for making the negative forms of these tenses, and for asking questions ('I do not like . . . Did he go? . . . It didn't work', etc.) They can also stand by themselves as main verbs, e.g. 'I do all the work', 'I did that picture'.

There are other, less common, auxiliary verbs, in particular MAY and MIGHT; SHOULD and WOULD.

They are used to make what is sometimes called the *subjunctive* or *conditional* forms of the verb (not very common in modern English). When they are used they suggest there is some doubt about whether or not the particular action does or does not really happen.

Look at these examples:—
I *may* possibly go. She said she *might* go. If you left me, I *should* die. Surely he *would* not do that, *would* he?

The difference between MAY and MIGHT is that MAY is usually referring to present or future time, MIGHT to past time.

The basic difference between WOULD and SHOULD is similar to that between WILL and SHALL, the auxiliary verbs of the future tense. (See Factsheet Nineteen.) But SHOULD also gives an idea of *ought,* while WOULD suggests *possibility.* So it is quite correct to write 'I would, we would' when these forms suit the sense.

There are other auxiliaries, like CAN and COULD which tell you whether a thing is *able to be done.* OUGHT, MUST and HAVE TO tell you whether a thing *should be done.*

Try not to use CAN when you mean 'being allowed to': use MAY instead.

Finally, you can say I AM GOING TO do something, instead of I SHALL; and I USED TO do something, instead of I WAS.

(a) Write out the following sentences, and after each, write the TENSE of the main verb. (Remember that the tense of the verb will be shown by the auxiliary. It might help you to look back at Factsheet Twenty-two, where all the tenses are set out).

(1) Father is baking a cake.

(2) Mother has just left for the office.

(3) My writing was awful.

(4) How did you do that?

(5) Sam, have you seen Jack?

(6) Whenever will they leave?

(7) I had always relied on Mrs Ellis.

(8) The plumbers will have finished soon.

(9) We were being particularly good.

(10) Whose bag is this?

(11) "Shall I compare thee to a summer's day?"

(12) He is being pursued by a bear.

(13) How many times have you been married?

(14) The enemy advanced in good order.

(15) We shall not be beaten by United this time.

(16) I have found a real bargain.

(17) Yes, you have a real bargain there.

(18) Are we going to try to save her?

(19) Too late; she will have been killed already.

(20) We might have reached her in time.

(20)

(b) In the following sentences a gap has been left where an auxiliary verb should be. Write them out, inserting an auxiliary verb that makes sense.

(1) We .... all been exceptionally good today.

(2) I .... not be leaving until tomorrow.

(3) "I .... fed up," shouted Mr Sanders.

(4) Once that machine gun post .... been captured we shall be able to advance.

(5) I .... chosen Josephine's entry, because it was the best.

(6) I .... not take any action until I was certain of the facts.

(7) If you would wait for me, I .... soon be ready.

(8) Though you .... kill him, he will not have died in vain.

(9) I .... driving steadily down the hill, when the front wheel came off.

(10) "Please, Miss, ... I be excused?"

(10)

(c) Read through this passage, then make two lists, (1) All the MAIN verbs, and (2) All the AUXILIARY verbs. If a word occurs more than once, list it each time.

Louise could not work properly. She had tried the sitting room, until her brother turned the television on. While she was transferring her books to the dining room, her mother told her that she was expecting guests that night, so Louise could not work in there.

"May I use the kitchen then?" she asked.

"Of course not," her mother answered. "I shall be cooking a meal here. Don't get in my way, dear. Surely you can go upstairs!" Upstairs, her own room was being decorated by her father; her brother's room was full of toys, which he was reorganizing, — and her father told her he did not want her in her parents' room. Then he promptly went into the bathroom. That was the last straw. Louise collected her books, descended the stairs again, and went out into the garden.

"Will you make room for me in there, Fang?" she said to the dog in his kennel.

(Note:— Write the main verbs in the form they appear in the passage, or in the infinitive. You should have found 25 main verbs, and 15 auxiliary verbs!)

(40)

FACTSHEET TWENTY-FOUR

VERBS, NOUNS & ADJECTIVES

We have now done a very large amount of work on the numerous different forms the verb can take. Now we need to look at verbs together with the other two major parts of speech — nouns and adjectives.

First a reminder of which is which:—

NOUN	A naming word, standing for a person, place or thing
ADJECTIVE	A describing word
VERB	A doing word.

What part of speech a word is depends on the job it is doing in the sentence. Very many words in English can be more than one part of speech; you have to decide which, at any given time, by looking closely at the function they are performing. Here are some examples:—

Turn on the *light*. (NOUN)   This bag is *light*. (ADJECTIVE)

I am going on a *run*. (NOUN)   We shall *run* to the top of the hill. (VERB)

Everyone knows that a *fly* can *fly*. (First time NOUN, second time VERB)

Glance back at Factsheets Fourteen and Fifteen. You will see that nouns can be formed from adjectives, and adjectives from nouns.

In the same way, nouns can be formed from verbs. You have already seen one example above:— 'To run' makes the identical noun 'a run'. There are others which are similar:— 'To act' and 'an act'; 'to judge' and 'a judge'; 'to laugh' and 'a laugh'.

Other verbs form nouns by changing the spelling of the word. For example:—

To choose	— Choice	To feed	— Food	To prove	— Proof
To see	— Sight	To grow	— Growth	To warm	— Warmth
To fly	— Flight	To believe	— Belief	To speak	— Speech
	(as well as 'a fly')	To hate	— Hatred	To think	— Thought
To weigh	— Weight	To live	— Life	To sing	— Song

Most verbs form nouns by adding an ENDING. The most common endings are in -TION, -SION and -ATION, but there are very many others. Here are some of them:—

To act	— Action	To decide	— Decision	To judge	— Judgment
	(as well as 'an act')	To provide	— Provision		(as well as 'a judge')
To move	— Motion	To enter	— Entrance	To form	— Formation
To please	— Pleasure	To arrive	— Arrival	To receive	— Reception
To succeed	— Success	To marry	— Marriage	To compare	— Comparison

Parts of verbs can also be *used* as nouns. The infinitive can be used as a noun:—

In 'To fly is glorious' the infinitive 'to fly' is acting as a 'verbal noun'.

The form of the verb ending -ING, which you have already met as the present participle can also act as a noun (strictly speaking known as a 'gerund'):—

In 'Flying is glorious' the word 'flying' is a noun, and, like 'to fly' in the previous example, is the subject of the sentence.

The participles, both present (TALKING) and past (TALKED), are also very often found being used as ADJECTIVES.

In 'I was flying', 'flying' is obviously part of a compound verb. In 'A flying brick hit me on the head', 'flying' is being used as an adjective.

Similarly, in 'I have chosen', 'chosen' is part of the compound verb; but in 'I bid you welcome our chosen candidate' it is an adjective describing 'candidate'.

Look at these three examples:—

The birds were singing sweetly. (SINGING is part of a compound verb).

I wandered among the singing birds. (SINGING is an adjective describing the birds).

I listened to the singing of the birds. (SINGING is a noun; it is the *thing* I listened to).

(a) Copy down these sentences, and next to each one write whether the word underlined is being used as a noun, a verb, or an adjective.

(1) I <u>fear</u> for her safety.

(2) Have no <u>fear,</u> I am here.

(3) He gave an evil <u>laugh.</u>

(4) It only hurts when I <u>laugh.</u>

(5) I <u>long</u> for a cream cake.

(6) I shall have to wait a <u>long</u> time for it.

(7) Perhaps I should eat a <u>sweet</u> instead.

(8) I prefer <u>sweet</u> things to savoury things.

(9) <u>Wait</u> for me, please.

(10) I do not want a long <u>wait.</u>

(10)

(b) Form a noun from each of the following verbs. (Some may of course stay the same!)

(1) feed

(2) hate

(3) run

(4) live

(5) hope

(6) laugh (TWO)

(7) think

(8) sting

(9) expect

(10) judge (TWO)

(11) regret

(12) decide

(13) arrange

(14) sleep

(15) enter

(16) seize

(17) obey

(18) believe

(19) receive

(20) conceal

(21) touch

(22) create

(23) expand

(24) postpone

(25) enjoy (TWO)

(26) examine

(27) close

(30)

(c) Read through the following passage. Then go through it carefully, and make three lists, one for NOUNS, one for VERBS and one for ADJECTIVES. Write down every verb, noun and adjective in the correct list. Count infinitives as verbs. Treat compound verbs as one single verb, and write down the words in the form they occur in the passage. (Clue: there are seventeen nouns, fourteen verbs, and nine adjectives).

The monster entered the gloomy den. Evil, green eyes flickered across the waiting victims. They were shaking in terror. They had abandoned all hope of rescue, as the thing began to advance upon them. The growling voice struck dread into them, as its eyes seemed to pierce into their hearts. What awful words would it utter?

"Open your books, then. Get ready. It is time to start the next lesson," said Mr White.

(20 — ½ each)

(d) Copy down the following sentences into your book. In each you will see the present or past participle forms, usually ending in -ING or -ED. In each case they may be used as a noun, an adjective, or part of a compound verb. At the end of each sentence write how it is being used in that particular case (NOUN, ADJECTIVE, PART OF VERB).

(1) The birds were *singing* happily in the trees.

(2) The constant *singing* of those birds is not doing anything for my headache.

(3) I therefore declare Mr Augustus Thistlebotham the duly *elected* candidate for Slugborough South West.

(4) *Spelling* has always been my biggest problem.

(5) A tree has been *planted* by the Lady Mayor to commemorate the event.

(6) The *waiting* gunman watched as his victim walked up the path.

(7) The *written* word is more enduring than the spoken.

(8) We have *made* our decision.

(9) Try some of my home-*made* toffee.

(10) *Angling* is my favourite pastime.

(20 — 2 each)

FACTSHEET TWENTY-FIVE

ADVERBS

You have already seen that an adjective is added to a noun to describe it. The adverb does much the same thing, but instead of being added to a noun, it is added to a verb (as you can see from its name). An adverb tells you the way in which the action of the verb is carried out.

Here are some examples:—

He ran (verb) *fast* (adverb). *She sings* (verb) *sweetly* (adverb). *You frequently* (adverb) *sigh* (verb).

Most adverbs are formed by adding LY to an adjective:—

Quick (adjective) — Quickly (adverb); Slow (adjective) — Slowly (adverb).

If the adjective ends in -Y already, change the Y to I, and then add LY. (Happy — Happily).

Beware:— Not all words ending in -LY are adverbs. 'Ugly', for example, is an adjective.
Remember, the way to tell what part of speech a word is, is to see what job it is doing in the sentence. In 'The ugly man snarled angrily', 'ugly', is obviously describing the noun, 'man'; it is not describing the verb 'snarled'. There is an adverb, 'angrily' which tells you the way he was snarling!

Not all adverbs end in -LY. The following are all adverbs that do not end in -LY. But, this is a double beware! Some of them can be either adverbs or adjectives, depending what job they are doing in the sentence.

FAST   HARD   LATE   WELL   MUCH   SOON   FAR

There are various TYPES of adverbs. Here are some examples of each type:—

Adverbs of MANNER	(The most common, telling you the way the action is done, and answering the question HOW?)
	slowly, surely, badly, well, happily, sadly, easily, hard, horribly.
Adverbs of DEGREE	(answering the question HOW MUCH? — or 'to what extent?')
	almost, rather, enough, very, too, much, only, also.
Adverbs of NUMBER	(answering the question HOW OFTEN?)
	once, twice, thrice, seldom, often, always, never, frequently.
Adverbs of TIME	(answering the question WHEN?)
	before, since, already, soon, then, seldom, now.
Adverbs of PLACE	(answering the question WHERE?)
	here, there, onward, northward, outward, inside, everywhere, nowhere.

Adverbs of AFFIRMATION and DENIAL (which sound more complicated than they are!)
yes, no, not, certainly, probably, perhaps.

In addition to the above, the QUESTION WORDS are also ADVERBS:—
how, how far, how often, how long, how soon,
why, when, where, whence, whither, whenever.

Note: 'Where' can also be a kind of adverb when it is not used to ask a question, but in sentences like: 'That is *where* we found the body, inspector'.)

Finally, adverbs have another use, as well as describing verbs. They can also be added to adjectives. They can 'modify' adjectives to make changes or additions to their meaning. The adverb VERY is very frequently used in this way, as in 'a very silly boy', 'a very good thing'. Many others are used in the same way, frequently with adjectives formed from verbs:—

'*slowly* spreading clouds, good *enough* for me, the *unanimously* elected chairman, *too* naughty for words, *rather* lazy, *completely* ridiculous, *utterly* ruined, *slightly* damaged'.

(a) A list of adjectives is written out below. From each adjective form an adverb. (Remember that sometimes the adverb can be the same as the adjective.)

(1)	quick	(8)	probable	(15)	high (TWO)
(2)	fast	(9)	early	(16)	loud (TWO)
(3)	slow	(10)	enough	(17)	first (TWO)
(4)	sudden	(11)	simple		
(5)	sure	(12)	much		
(6)	bad	(13)	whole		
(7)	good	(14)	holy		

(20)

(b) In the following sentences, underline every word that is used as an adverb.
(Remember that not all adverbs end in -LY, and check the Factsheet for words which may not at first glance look like adverbs, but in fact are!)

(1) "How often have I told you to work more carefully?" Miss Piltdown shouted angrily.   (FOUR)

(2) There, lurking loathsomely behind his raised desk lid, was the bully of the second form, 'Ugly' Joe Crocker.   (TWO)

(3) Mandy struck the ball forcibly and began to run fast, only to discover immediately, by falling flat on her face, that her shoe laces had been tied tightly together by that slimy toad, Mavis.   (SEVEN)

(4) Barbara had deliberately decided that she was not going to give that 'awfully nice', but terribly boring boy, Michael, any more opportunities to engage her in conversation.   (FIVE)

(5) "Get your lovely oranges here! Cheapest you'll find anywhere in town!"   (TWO)

(6) "Yes, we have no bananas today."   (THREE)

(7) I could see him clearly, although he was walking quickly along the very edge of the beach, and frequently gazing around him.   (THREE)

(8) How certain are you of the place where you left the body?   (TWO)

(9) Surely that is not the baby crying again!   (TWO)

(30)

(c) In each of these sentences there is only ONE adverb. Copy the sentences, write the adverb at the end, and CLASSIFY it, as an adverb of manner, degree, place, etc. (or as a question word).

(1) Can you see them coming yet?   (6) How could you do that to me?
(2) That is too good to be true.   (7) Your writing is very good, Tina.
(3) I am feeling slightly sick.   (8) I seldom visit the ballet.
(4) He had scattered ink everywhere.   (9) Here you are, sonny, one cornet.
(5) Yes, it is David in the lead!   (10) I've seen that film before.

(20 — 1 for identification, 1 for classification.)

(d) In this passage the adverbs are missing. Write it out, inserting adverbs that make good sense in the spaces.

The two boys walked .... down the dark passage. .... was a sound, echoing .... in the remote distance. They tried .... to ignore it, but it would not go .... In fact, though they hated to admit it, it was getting .... and .... louder. They looked around them .... for a place to hide. .... could they escape? One of them spotted a hollow, in the clammy surface of the wall. They stumbled into it .... in time. The 'thing' roared by them.

"That's the last time I go potholing with you in a railway tunnel," Stuart told William ....

(10)

FACTSHEET TWENTY-SIX

COMPARISON

All the adjectives and adverbs we have talked about so far have been in what is known as the POSITIVE form. There are two other forms, the COMPARATIVE and the SUPERLATIVE. You can say something is 'small' for example, but you may want to say that it is 'rather small', or 'more small' — compared with something else. You may also want to say that it is 'very small', or 'the most small' of a group. Most adjectives have special forms to show this sort of comparison. They are formed by adding -ER or -EST. Here are some examples:—

POSITIVE — small   COMPARATIVE — smaller   SUPERLATIVE — smallest;

big, bigger, biggest; great, greater, greatest; slow, slower, slowest; high, higher, highest.

The comparative (ending in -ER) is used when you are talking about *two* things; the superlative when it is a larger number. (Remember it as '-ER two, -EST three'.)

So you would say:— 'Of Jack and Jill, Jack is the brighter; but of Tom, Dick and Harry, Tom is the brightest'.

Unfortunately, not all adjectives form their comparatives and superlatives in the above manner.

For those that end in -E, you simply add -R and -ST as you would expect; for those that end in -Y, you change the Y to I and then add -ER or -EST.

For long words (those with several syllables) and any words where it would be difficult to pronounce the comparative or superlative if you added -ER and -EST, simply put MORE and MOST in front of the adjective:—

beautiful, more beautiful, most beautiful (not *beautifuler, beautifulest*).

Simply go by your common sense, and choose what sounds right.

There are also IRREGULAR comparisons.

Here are some examples:—

POSITIVE	COMPARATIVE	SUPERLATIVE	POSITIVE	COMPARATIVE	SUPERLATIVE
Happy	Happier	Happiest	Good	Better	Best
Grey	Greyer	Greyest	Bad	Worse	Worst
Clever	{ More Clever / Cleverer	{ Most Clever / Cleverest	Much } Many }	More	Most
Famous	More Famous	Most Famous	Old	{ Older / Elder	{ Oldest / Eldest
Little	{ Littler / Less	{ Littlest / Least	Late	{ Later / Latter	{ Latest / Last

(Note:— 'later, latest' refer to differences in time; 'latter, last' to differences in position. 'Elder' and 'eldest' are only used of people; and now are often only used in referring to members of the family:— 'elder brother, eldest sister' etc.)

There are also comparative and superlative forms of adverbs. Only adverbs of quality are really involved, and almost ALL adverbs that end in -LY (the vast majority) form their comparative and superlative by adding MORE and MOST: *wisely, more wisely, most wisely.*

Adverbs of only one syllable add -ER and -EST as if they were adjectives, and some adverbs are irregular. Here are some examples:—

Well — Better — Best; Badly — Worse — Worst; Fast — Faster — Fastest.

(a) Write down the COMPARATIVE form of the following adjectives and adverbs. Next to each answer say whether the original word is an adjective, or an adverb, — or whether it could be either, depending on how it was used in the sentence.

(1) Suspicious
(2) Badly
(3) Slowly
(4) Ugly
(5) Late (TWO)
(6) Silly
(7) Terrible
(8) Famous
(9) Idle

(10)

(b) This exercise is much the same, but instead of the comparative, write down the SUPERLATIVE form of each adjective and adverb; once again say whether the original word is adjective, adverb, or either.

(1) Old (TWO)
(2) Fast
(3) Easy
(4) Easily
(5) Little (TWO)
(6) Well
(7) Sadly
(8) Free

(10)

(c) Rewrite the following sentences, correcting the mistakes which have been made in using the comparative and superlative of adjectives and adverbs in them:—

(1) Luke is the most smallest boy in this class.
(2) Of the three girls, Jackie is the neater.
(3) She is happyest when she is working hard.
(4) This is the most easy exercise I have ever done.
(5) Sarah can run much more fastly than Tim.
(6) Of the two of them, Marcus is by far the brightest.
(7) Kevin does littler work than anyone else in this class.
(8) Caroline has many toys, but Mary has even manier.
(9) I think that this is the wetest day we have had all month.
(10) He has written the foolishest answer I have ever seen.

(10)

(d) Read the following passage. Then make lists for (1) all the adjectives and (2) all the adverbs in it. Write COMPARATIVE and SUPERLATIVE next to those which are in these forms.

The boy and girl watched idly from the side of the railway. A train coasted smoothly round the bend. The powerful locomotive was pulling more carriages than usual, but it still gained speed steadily. It was already going much faster as the downward gradient began, and it reached its greatest speed as it hurtled madly through the country station.

"Oh no, I'm sure there will be a most awful crash," said Kate, as she saw the carriages sway even more alarmingly. "Do something, Patrick."

"Don't worry," answered Patrick in a condescending voice that infuriated his younger sister. "It's getting slower now."

At that moment the engine left the tracks. The two children watched in horror as the whole train plunged from the embankment in the worst and most disastrous crash ever.

"It will serve you right if it's broken," said Kate as she picked up the engine.

(40 — 1 for each piece of information required)

FACTSHEET TWENTY-SEVEN

PREPOSITIONS, CONJUNCTIONS & INTERJECTIONS

Prepositions

'Pre' means 'in front of', — and position means position!

Prepositions stand in front of nouns to tell you position (in time as well as in space!)

Prepositions must refer to (sometimes called 'govern') a noun or pronoun. They cannot stand by themselves.

There are two types of preposition, those indicating PLACE, and those indicating TIME.

Here is a list of some of the common ones:—

In into on onto upon at under over above below by with from to for before behind about amid among along around across between without up down through past after before during until till inside outside within from in from under in between of off.

Many of these words can be adverbs as well as prepositions (and they may also be conjunctions as you will see in the next section). Remember, if the word is standing in front of or referring to a noun or pronoun, it is a preposition. If there is no noun or pronoun, you will probably find that the word concerned is an adverb.

For example:— 'He went in' ('in' is an adverb) and 'Look in the house' ('in' is a preposition referring to 'house'). 'A plane flew over' ('over' is an adverb, telling you where the flying was going on) and 'The plane flew over the house' ('over' is a preposition linked to 'house').

Be careful, though, as sometimes a preposition may be separated by one or two other words from the noun with which it goes.

Conjunctions

Conjunctions are JOINING or LINKING words.

Here is a list of some of the common ones:—

And but because so if although though therefore unless as than since while until for that after before as soon as as well as

They may link two nouns together. (E.g. The boys *and* the girls.)

They may link adjectives or adverbs. (E.g. A long *and* weary road.)

They may link two parts of a sentence together. (E.g. They started to run down the street *and* immediately the policeman started to chase them.)

Once again, some of the words used as conjunctions can also be used as other parts of speech, depending on what job they do in the sentence. Look at these examples:—

'I went for the doctor for grandma was feeling ill'. In this, the first 'for' is a preposition linked to the noun 'doctor'; the second 'for' is a conjunction joining two halves of the sentence together.

The most common conjunctions are AND and BUT. When you are joining two parts of a long sentence together, try to use different conjunctions — to add a little variety!

Interjections

These are words *spoken*, — often shouted, called out, or exclaimed. For example:— Oh! Ah! Argh! Alas! Ouch! Poo! They often have an exclamation mark (!). And they are the last of the parts of speech . . .

(a) Write out the following sentences, and underline the prepositions in each. (Remember that a word which looks like a preposition may be other things, — depending on its use in the sentence.)

   (1) She leapt into the water; her head appeared briefly above the waves, as she swam between the rocks and into the open sea.   (FOUR)

   (2) After she had been to the grocers, Jan went across the road to the fish and chip shop to buy dinner for the kids.   (FOUR)

   (3) She just managed to pull the pram back as the car screeched by, skidded round the corner and then came to an abrupt halt with a squeal of brakes.   (THREE)

   (4) I have told you over and over again:— write your name at the top of each page before you hand in your answers.   (TWO)

   (5) The ball flew through the window, smashing it into fragments which ripped the sofa, and then bounced off a vase of flowers which fell to the floor and spread a widening pool of water across the new carpet, before finally imbedding itself in a large bowl of fruit salad, the contents of which were now decorating the walls as a result of the ball's sudden arrival.   (ELEVEN)

   (6) Within the walls of the castle, the besieged forces waited behind the parapets and watched the enemy preparing their siege outside.   (TWO)

   (7) Before you go, have a look at this.   (ONE)

   (8) He went in and looked around, checking quickly that no-one was behind the door and glancing through the open window at the moonlit lawn.   (THREE)
                                                                                                            (30)

(b) Write out the following sentences, and this time underline all the conjunctions in each.

   (1) My father says that I must work hard or I will not get a bike for Christmas.   (TWO)

   (2) The snake sinuously and silently approached the unsuspecting victim as he sat beside the cooking pot.   (TWO)

   (3) He is quite clever although his sister is dim and his brother a complete idiot.   (TWO)

   (4) He jumped on me before I was ready, and I was forced to take evasive action.   (TWO)

   (5) While the cat's away, the mice will play.   (ONE)

   (6) As soon as she saw him, she burst into tears.   (ONE)
                                                                                                            (10)

(c) In this passage some prepositions and conjunctions have been missed out. Rewrite the passage, inserting prepositions or conjunctions that make the best sense.

   .... the interjection is a rare .... untamed part of speech, I often insert one ....
   my sentences. Things may have been dull .... it arrived, ... once it has barged its way
   .... the door and into the middle of the action, things become much more lively. It snubs the verbs
   .... abuses the adverbs .... hooting its own vulgar message .... the top ....
   its voice.

                                                                                                      (20 — 2 each)

Factsheets 1 to 7

(a) Here is a list of words. TEN of them could be nouns (though it may be possible for them to be other parts of speech as well). Find the ten words, and use each of them in a sentence of your own, as a noun. Remember it is the use a word is put to in a sentence that determines what part of speech it is.

thought	decided	incorrect	study	love	action	heard
manage	work	arrangement	soon	watch	Scotland	English
every	right	action	they	see	after	

(20 — 1 per word + 1 per sentence)

(b) Rewrite these sentences. In the spaces shown either insert the correct article (the, a, an) or if no article is needed, simply do not leave a space.

(1) All of .... girls in this class are clever, but Susan is .... cleverest.

(2) People who look after .... sheep are called .... shepherds.

(3) Do you take .... milk or .... lemon in your tea?

(4) He did not have .... answer to .... inspector's question.

(5) "............ ship has been struck by .... iceberg," shouted Captain Steerforth.

(10)

(c) In each of the following sentences, give the proper nouns their capital letters (which have been omitted). You are not recommended to believe quite what the sentences say.

(1) Gravity was invented by sir isaac newton; before that things could never fall down.

(2) The kettle was an early discovery of watt; it was later put on wheels by stephenson, a famous author.

(3) When christopher columbus discovered america in the atlantic ocean, it was entirely full of indians so he naturally thought it was indonesia.

(4) King william IV was famous for creating peers, but it was his brother, george, who created the first one at brighton in the english channel.

(5) john the baptist originally made a large profit by only eating insects, but finally lost his head over a dancing girl named baloney.

(20 — 1 each)

(d) In each of the following sentences there is one abstract noun and one collective noun. Write down the two nouns, clearly indicating which is which.

(1) A sudden peal of bells from the church steeple rang out through the silence.

(2) She drew a shaft from her quiver of arrows, fitted it to the bowstring and took careful aim at the tiny window.

(3) Before them a long flight of stairs led up into the impenetrable darkness.

(4) Hidden amid the bales of cotton, the runaway slave awaited his chance to run for the river boat.

(5) The event was rather spoilt by a plague of tourists.

(20 — 1 per word + 1 per correct identification)

(e) Abstract nouns are often formed by putting endings onto other words (such as verbs and adjectives). In this exercise you have to think of some with particular endings:—

(1) Five abstract nouns ending in -TION

(2) Five abstract nouns ending in -SION

(3) Five abstract nouns ending in -NESS

(4) Two abstract nouns ending in -MENT

(5) Two abstract nouns ending in -ANCE or -ENCE

(6) One abstract noun ending in -TH

(20 — 1 each)

Factsheets 8 to 15

(a) Give the plural of the following nouns:—

(1) party	(6) house	(11) hero	(16) tooth
(2) gas	(7) mouse	(12) piano	(17) brother-in-law
(3) valley	(8) box	(13) radio	(18) disability
(4) wolf	(9) roof	(14) church	(19) genius (TWO)
(5) woman	(10) goose	(15) salmon	

(20)

(b) Change these phrases into the possessive form (e.g. 'The book of the boy' would become 'The boy's book').

(1)   the light of the sun   (4)   the capture of the pass

(2)   the price of vegetables   (5)   the toys of the baby

(3)   the parties of the ladies

(10 — 2 each)

(c) The following list of words has masculine and feminine forms mixed up in it. For each word, if it is masculine, give its feminine equivalent; if it is feminine, make it masculine.

(1) king	(4) landlord	(7) stallion	(10) Paul
(2) waitress	(5) bachelor	(8) Girl Guide	
(3) mistress	(6) cow	(9) lad	

(10)

(d) Write out the following passage, and underline all the PRONOUNS in it. You should find twenty.

"Who are you?" he demanded. "And what is that in your hand?"
I gazed at him absently, as if he was talking to himself.
"Since it is mine, not yours, that is none of your business," I answered finally, pushing myself back against the wall. His face went red with anger.
"It looks like a gun to me," he snarled.
"No," I replied. "It's only a banana . . ."

(10 — ½ each)

(e) In each of the following there are two adjectives. For each question write out the two adjectives, and say whether they are adjectives of quality, quantity or distinction.

(1)   "This book is yours." — "Which book?" — "The one I have here."

(2)   You are in serious trouble, my friend.

(3)   Both goals were scored in the first half.

(4)   We were entirely alone in the little boat, amid the vastness of the sea.

(5)   "What name shall I put?" the sour-faced clerk demanded officiously.

(20 — 1 per adjective + 1 for correct classification.)

(f) The following words are nouns. Form adjectives from them by adding an ending. (You may have to make other changes to the spelling as well.)

(1) friend	(4) value	(7) hate	(10) noise
(2) volcano	(5) fortune	(8) fool	
(3) danger	(6) terror	(9) centre	

(10)

(g) This time you have been given the adjectives. Write down the nouns that 'go with' them.

(1) silly	(4) angry	(7) cruel	(10) true
(2) long	(5) brave	(8) alive	
(3) dead	(6) sad	(9) fierce	

(10)

TESTSHEET THREE

Factsheets 16 to 21

(a) Copy out these sentences, and underline the verbs in each. Remember that verbs may be made up of several words, and that these may be separated by other words which are not parts of the verb. Make sure you underline all parts of the verb, and not anything else.

(1)   That dog is constantly barking.

(2)   It chased the cat three times round the house this morning.

(3)   Perhaps I should feed it.

(4)   Kindly pay attention, girls.

(5)   She has been watching that clock for the past hour.

(6)   Necessity is the mother of invention.

(7)   What shall we do with a drunken sailor?

(8)   We are all waiting eagerly for your answer, William.

(9)   I have never liked that fellow Wood.

(10)   Wherever did I put that picture of my brother's hideous children?

(20 — 2 per correct verb)

(b) Read through the following sentences. Find the verb (which of course may be in several parts once again), write it down, and next to it write which tense it is in. Try to be as accurate as possible in giving the tense its correct name.

(1)   Are you being served?

(2)   Who has taken my book?

(3)   I shall be leaving tomorrow.

(4)   The bride and bridesmaids wore lemon yellow.

(5)   Once she had always walked to school.

(6)   Dad put the oil-can on the kitchen table.

(7)   That will have been the milkman wanting his money no doubt.

(8)   Across the shining sea the last gleams of the sunset were slowly and imperceptibly fading into the darkness of night.

(9)   In the gathering twilight the gentle breezes whispered in the branches of the palm trees above.

(10)   Down those sands to the water's edge they had often, in the dim forgotten past, walked together through the scented shades of night.

(20 — 1 per verb + 1 per tense)

(c) Rewrite the following sentences in the tense indicated at the end of each.

(1)   I have often walked down this street before. (Past — simple)

(2)   Once a jolly swagman camped by a billabong. (Pluperfect)

(3)   Shall I compare thee to a summer's day? (Perfect)

(4)   Mine eyes have seen the glory of the coming of the Lord. (Present continuous)

(5)   She wheeled her wheelbarrow through streets broad and narrow. (Future)

(6)   The ploughman homeward plods his weary way. (Imperfect)

(7)   Where did you get that hat? (Perfect)

(8)   The nightingales are singing and the white moon beams. (TWO — Imperfect & Past (simple))

(9)   In Xanadu did Kubla Khan a stately pleasure dome decree. (Future)

(20 — 2 each)

(d) For each of the following verbs write both the past tense (simple) and the past participle:—

(1)   do   (6)   freeze   (11)   shake

(2)   sing   (7)   lie   (12)   draw

(3)   shut   (8)   lay   (13)   fly

(4)   stand   (9)   bring   (14)   hide

(5)   choose   (10) forget   (15)   see

(30 — 1 for each required)

Factsheets 22 to 27

(a)   The following sentences have verbs in the active voice. Rewrite the sentences, keeping the same meaning, with the verbs in the passive. (You will have to make other changes as well.)

    (1)   The ball smashed the large window into fragments.

    (2)   Dad will do the shopping this afternoon.

    (3)   Sharon saw the burglar climbing in through the window.

    (4)   Has anyone told mum that Billy is painting the shed? (TWO verbs to change)

                                  (10 — 2 per verb)

(b)   This is the reverse. Change the verbs in these sentences from passive to active, while keeping the same meaning for the sentence. (Once again you will have to make quite a few changes.)

    (1)   All the cooking was done with my microwave.

    (2)   The aspidistra has been knocked over by Edward.

    (3)   Mr Sawyer was unanimously elected as leader by the party.

    (4)   She has been stabbed through the heart with a knife.

    (5)   The ground is prepared for a second crop by ploughing.

                                  (10 — 2 per sentence)

(c)   Read through the following five sentences. Then make two lists, one of *main verbs,* and one of *auxiliary verbs.* (Remember there can be more than one auxiliary with a main verb, and not all verbs need any auxiliary.)

    (1)   Where have you put the cornflakes?

    (2)   I would have seen him if he had been there.

    (3)   If you want a smack, Oliver, you are going about it the right way.

    (4)   I see that Christopher and Alison are squabbling again.

    (5)   She should have arrived on the early flight, but it was delayed by fog over Manchester, and will now land at Prestwick at eight o'clock.

                                (20 — 1 per verb in the correct list)

(d)   Form nouns from the following verbs:—

(1) arrive	(4) prove	(7) see	(10) enter
(2) decide	(5) heat	(8) deceive	
(3) arrange	(6) speak	(9) entertain	

                                  (10)

(e)   Read carefully through the following sentences, and make a list of all the adverbs you can find in them.

    (1)   He stealthily crept in, hoping the teacher would not notice him.

    (2)   "Come here immediately," she said, looking up at the wrong moment.

    (3)   I have told you before about that terrible writing, Jonathan.

    (4)   I have almost never seen anything so scruffy.

    (5)   Whoever taught you to write like that?

                                  (10 — 1 per adverb)

(f)   Give the comparative and superlative forms of each of the following adjectives and adverbs:—

(1) wet	(4) fast	(7) tiny	(10) many
(2) alone	(5) good	(8) badly	
(3) impossible	(6) well	(9) extreme	

                                  (20 — 1 per form)

(g)   Read this passage, then make two lists, — one of all the *prepositions* in it, the other of all the *conjunctions.*

    Although he could see the car from the window and it was obviously empty, he went upstairs to his bedroom to find the binoculars. Through them, as well as the package on the back seat, he could also see something else, — but not what he had expected. As he watched, a hand reached into the car . . .

                                    (10 — 1 per word)

Revision Test

(a) For each of the following sentences, (i) say what TENSES the verbs are in, and (ii) rewrite the sentences with the verbs in the tenses stated at the end.

    (1)   I am waiting for Bradley. (IMPERFECT.)

    (2)   He has been jumping on the furniture. (PLUPERFECT — continuous form.)

    (3)   Then he was making faces at me through the window. (PAST (simple)).

    (4)   When he comes back, I want to see him. (TWO:— PERFECT and FUTURE in that order).

    (10)

(b) (i) Rewrite these phrases using the possessive form:—

    (1)   the curls of the girls   (3)   the cream of the class   (5)   the mother of the children

    (2)   the lair of the foxes   (4)   the might of Germany

    (ii) Rewrite the following possessive phrases. Change the plural words in them to the singular — and the singular words to the plural.

    (6)   the boy's book   (8)   the woman's child   (10) the wolf's cry

    (7)   the geese's owners   (9)   the roof's chimney

    (10)

(c) Give both the past tense (simple) and the past participle of each of the following verbs:—

    (1) blow   (3) rise   (5) tear   (7) swim   (9) begin

    (2) write   (4) speak   (6) know   (8) drink   (10) wear

    (10)

(d) In the following sentences the capital letters have been omitted. Rewrite them, inserting the capital letters in the correct places.

    (1)   The titanic, white star line's flagship, was sunk by an iceberg in the atlantic ocean while on her maiden voyage from southampton.

    (2)   The french language remained predominant in alsace-lorraine throughout the four and a half years of the german occupation.

    (3)   The takeover bid by grabbit and run properties ltd. for messrs. gently and sleeping is to go before the monopolies commission.

    (20 — 1 per capital)

(e) Here is a list of six adjectives. For each write down the comparative and superlative forms, and also an adverb that can be formed from the adjective. Note that for the last one you need to give TWO forms of the comparative and superlative.

    (1) good   (2) bad   (3) beautiful   (4) fast   (5) nasty   (6) late (Two forms of the comparative and superlative)

    (10 — ½ per correct word)

(f) Write out all the *conjunctions,* and all the *prepositions* in the following sentences, making it clear which word is a preposition and which a conjunction. You should find five of each altogether.

    (1)   He peeped round the door, although it was risky.

    (2)   After she had said that, there was a terrible song and dance about it.

    (3)   The victim was tied to a table, while over her a giant axe hung suspended.

    (4)   I sprang for the chandelier as soon as he drew his sword.

    (10)

Revision Test

(a) State whether each of the following sentences is, in its present form, a statement, question, or command (and if it is the negative form of one of these, include that information too). Then rewrite each sentence to change it into the form stated at the end.

(1) You do not like Jelly, Amanda.   (Change to a Question.)
(2) Are you doing the exercise?   (Change to a Negative Command.)
(3) Isn't Stuart a clever boy?   (Change to a Positive Statement.)
(4) Wait for them here; or are you staying with us? (TWO:— Change to a Question and a Negative Command in that order.)

(10)

(b) Give the plural forms of the following nouns:—

(1) mass   (3) wife   (5) louse   (7) trousers   (9) mother-in-law
(2) silence   (4) child   (6) salmon   (8) radio   (10) entity

(10)

(c) Some of the following sentences are in the passive, some are in the active voice. Rewrite each of them; if it is active, change it to passive; if it is passive, change it to active; but in either case, keep the meaning roughly the same.

(1) Will Sandra choose Gwen for the team this time?
(2) By whom had that book been written?
(3) Has her pen been lost again?
(4) Matthew's father is chasing him round the garden.
(5) The rope was severed with an axe.

(15 — 3 per sentence)

(d) Give the collective nouns for groups of the following:—

(1) cattle   (2) lions   (3) bees   (4) directors   (5) angels

Give the feminine form of the following masculine nouns:—

(6) actor   (7) nephew   (8) headmaster (9) drake   (10) brave

(10)

(e) In each of the following sentences are two abstract nouns, which have been underlined. Rewrite the sentences (and you will have to change them completely) to keep the same approximate meaning, but using the abstract nouns to form other parts of speech — verbs, adjectives, or even adverbs. The parts of speech you might form from the two words are suggested at the end of each sentence, but if you can do it using others, by all means do so.

(1) They showed amazement at the simplicity of it.   (Adjective/Adjective)
(2) Silence from his pupils is a requirement of Mr Johnson   (Adjective/Verb)
(3) Life holds no joy for me.   (Adjective/Verb)
(4) Further delay may cause our capture.   (Verb/Verb)
(5) Mary has great ability in mathematics.   (Adjective/Adverb)

(15 — 3 per sentence)

(f) In the following sentences, write out the words that have been underlined, and next to each word write what part of speech it is being used as. (CLUE:— there are only three different parts of speech involved.)

(1) Which girl said that.   (4) It is high time you helped yourself.
(2) Here are your books.   (5) Where is the boy who said that he had been hurt?
(3) Who could have done this thing?

(10)

61

INDEX AND SUMMARY

Interjections	Words shouted or exclaimed.	Factsheet 27
Irregular Verbs	Verbs where the past tense and/or past participle are not formed in the usual way (by adding -ED), but by changing the spelling of the verb, adding a different ending etc. Many common verbs are irregular.	21
Masculine/Feminine Forms	Some nouns have different masculine and feminine forms depending on whether the person or animal referred to is male or female.	10
the Negative	Formed by inserting NOT in the continuous or emphatic forms of the tenses.	17
Nouns	Nouns are naming words; words that stand for things, people, animals and places.	1 & 2
Nouns from Adjectives	The addition of an ending to adjectives (usually adjectives of quality) to form nouns (usually abstract nouns). The most common ending is -NESS; other endings are:— -TY -CY -ENCE/ANCE -MENT -DOM -HOOD -ICE -TH	15
Nouns from Verbs	the addition of an ending to the verb, often involving other changes in spelling, to form a noun. Some endings are the same as for nouns formed from adjectives (see immediately above); but the most common are -TION, -SION, -ATION.	24
Nouns used as Adjectives	Nouns put with other nouns to describe them.	14
the Passive	The form ('voice') of a verb where the action returns to the subject. Formed with the verb 'to be' as the auxiliary. Tenses:— I am liked; I shall be liked; I was liked; I have been liked; I had been liked, etc.	22
Past Tense (Aorist)	The most common form of the verb used to express action in the past (in writing). Formed by adding -ED to the verb; but there are also many verbs that have irregular past tenses.	20
Past Participle	Used to make the perfect (and other) tenses; also as an adjective. Formed by adding -ED to the verb (though there are also many verbs with irregular past participles).	20
Perfect Tense	Used to show completed action in the past. Formed with the auxiliary verb HAS/HAVE + the past participle.	20
Persons of the Verb	These are indicated by the pronoun:— 1st. person singular — I like; 2nd. sing. — you like; 3rd. sing. — he/she/it likes; 1st. plural — we like; 2nd. plur. — you like; 3rd. plur. — they like. All noun subjects are 3rd. person.	16
the Plural	Plural means more than one.	8
Plural endings of nouns	Most nouns form their plural by adding -S. Nouns ending in Y, change the Y to I and add -ES (except those ending in AY, EY, OY, UY, which just add -S). Nouns ending in S, SS, SH, CH, X add -ES. Nouns ending in O add -ES (except those ending in EO, IO, OO, and one or two others, which just add -S). Some nouns ending in F change F to V and add -ES. Some nouns ending in FE also change F to V and add -S. Some nouns change their form for the plural, and there are various unusual forms.	8